D0549328

Nelson Advanced Modular Science

ITEM   018 045 168

Structure, Bonding and the Periodic Table

UXBRIDGE COLLEGE LEARNING CENTRE
Park Road, Uxbridge, Middlesex UB8 1NQ
Telephone: 01895 853326

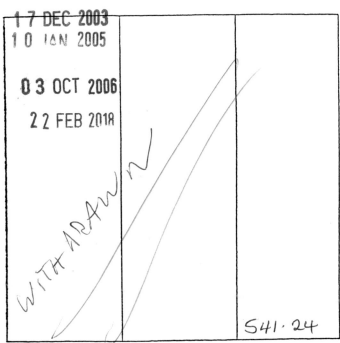

Thomas Nelson and Sons Ltd
Nelson House Mayfield Road
Walton-on-Thames Surrey
KT12 5PL UK

Thomas Nelson Australia
102 Dodds Street
South Melbourne
Victoria 3205 Australia

Nelson Canada
1120 Birchmount Road
Scarborough Ontario
MIK 5G4 Canada

First published by Thomas Nelson and Sons Ltd 1996
I(T)P Thomas Nelson is an International Thomson Publishing Company
I(T)P is used under licence

ISBN 0-17-448256-6
NPN 9 8 7 6 5 4 3 2 1

Acknowledgements:
Acquisitions: Chris Coyer
Administration: Jenny Goode
Editorial Management: Simon Bell/Sharon Jordan
Marketing: Jane Lewis
Production: Liam Reardon
Design: Maria Pritchard
Typesetting and illustration: Hardlines, Charlbury, Oxford
Printed in Spain

Contents

General Introduction v

1 Atomic structure 1

Preamble 1
 Introduction 1
 The (much shortened) history 2
Particles and structure 5
 The particles 5
 The nucleus 5
 Isotopes 5
The mass spectrometer 5
 The machine 5
 Mass spectra 7
Radioactivity 8
 Radioactive decay 9
 Nuclear equations 11
 Nuclear reactions 12
 Nuclear fusion 13
 Half-life 13
 Uses of radioactive isotopes 14
Ionisation energy 15
 Ionisation energy and the periodic table 16
 The 'aufbau' principle 17
 Atomic orbitals 20
Electron affinity 21

2 Quantitative chemistry 22

Empirical and molecular formulae 22
Equations 23
 Ionic equations 24
Reacting masses 25
 The Avogadro constant and the mole 25
 Reacting masses 26
Use of concentrations: volumetric analysis 27
 Acid/base titrations 27
 Other titrations 32
Problems involving gas volumes 32

3 Bonding and structure 34

Bonds 34
The ionic bond 34
 Ions 34
 Features favouring ionic bonding 35
The covalent bond 36
 The sharing of electrons 36
 Orbitals and covalent bonds 37
 Polarity in bonds and in molecules 38
Intermolecular forces 39

Hydrogen bonding   39
Dipole–dipole forces   40
Dispersion forces   41
Bonding and properties   41
Giant molecular forces   41
Ionic substances   41
Molecular covalent substances   42
Polymers   42
Intermolecular forces in the liquid state   43
Change of state   44
The hydration of ions in solution and the solubility
of ionic compounds   44
The shapes of molecules and ions   46
Metallic bonding   48

4 Oxidation/reduction and the transition metals   50

Oxidation and reduction   50
Definitions   50
Oxidation numbers   50
Oxidation numbers and redox reactions   52
The transition metals   55
The d-block and transition metals   55
Electron structures and variable oxidation numbers   55
Formation of complex ions   57
Coloured ions   57
Paramagnetism in ions   58
The action of alkali on aqua complexes   58
Vanadium   61
Iron   62
Catalytic activity and the transition elements   63

5 The Periodic Table   65

The Mendeleyev table   65
Aspects of the chemistry of period 3: sodium to chlorine 65
Reactions of the elements   67
The oxides of Period 3   69
The chlorides of Period 3   70
Groups 1 and 2: the s-block   71
Flame colours   72
The elements of group 2   73
The oxides of group 2   73
The chlorides of Groups 1 and 2   74
Solubility trends in the sulphates and hydroxides of Group 2   74
Trends in thermal stabilities of carbonates and nitrates of
Groups 1 and 2   75
Group 4   76
The elements   77
The oxides of Group 4   77
The chlorides of Group 4   79
Oxidation states in Group 4   80

Introduction

This textbook is one of a series of four produced in response to a demand from students and their teachers for resource material in support of the chemistry courses which lead to examinations set by the University of London Examination and Assessment Council in the new modular format. There has been a widespread development of modular courses at Advanced level, and ULEAC took this step in September 1994. There is also an ever-present pressure on syllabus writers to introduce new material into syllabuses to ensure that they reflect adequately the role of chemistry in society today, yet the principal core concepts laid down by common agreement and the School Curriculum and Assessment Authority must retain their rightful place. Writers of the new syllabus and these texts have endeavoured to balance these conflicting demands.

There is a bewildering variety of chemistry texts discussing aspects of the subject at an appropriate level for the A-level student, and it is not the intention of this series to divert the attention of students from these. Indeed it is hoped that students will be excited by their study of chemistry and will want to pursue specialist avenues of interest, as countless others have done in years past. However, it is recognised that at certain times students seek a text which will encapsulate in a relatively small volume the outline of necessary study for each of the ULEAC modules in chemistry.

These volumes are written by the examiners, all experienced teachers, specifically to prepare students for these examinations, and all the necessary basic material of the syllabus is covered. They further prompt and give pointers for further study for the interested student.

We hope that students will find these texts helpful and supportive of their studies at A-level and their preparation for examinations, and also stimulating to further reading in a wider context.

Geoff Barraclough
Chemistry Series Editor

The author
Dr Rod Beavon is a Chief Examiner and Head of Science at Westminster School, London.

Acknowledgements

The authors and publishers are grateful to the following for permission to reproduce copyright material.

Photographs

Image Select/Ann Ronan Picture Library: Figure 1.1, page 2 (originally appeared in Muspratt, S. *Chemistry*, London, 1860); Figure 1.3, page 2; Figure 1.5, page 4; Figure 1.20, page 13; Figure 1.9, page 5; Figure 3.7, page 37 (by permission of the Nobel Foundation); Figure 3.17(b), page 46 (originally appeared in Thorpe, E. *The History of Chemistry*, London, 1910); Figure 5.1, page 65 (originally appeared in Thorpe, E. *The History of Chemistry*, London, 1910)

Department of Physics, Imperial College/Science Photo Library: Figure 1.6, page 4

James Holmes/Oxford Centre for Molecular Sciences/Science Photo Library: Figure 1.11, page 7

Dr Jurgen Scriba/Science Photo Library: Figure 1.15, page 9

Science Photo Library: Figure 1.17, page 10

Martin Dohrn/Science Photo Library: Figure 1.22, page 15

Alfred Pasieka/Science Photo Library: Figure 3.1, page 34

Adam Hart Davis/Science Photo Library: Figure 3.5, page 37

Alain Morvan/Gamma: Figure 3.14(a), page 41

Jerry Mason/Science Photo Library: Figure 5.5 (b), (c), (d), (e), (f), page 72

CNRI/Science Photo Library: Figure 5.6, page 75

Atomic structure

Preamble

Introduction

As you start this book, and probably the whole course, you may wonder what there is to be learned on the structure of atoms that is new. Maybe you feel you have already done it all. During the next months and years you will be learning more chemistry, but when you study a science, unlike say learning a language, the ideas which you already have about the world are modified and replaced by those which are presently accepted by scientists generally.

That is what we mean, at A level, by being 'right'; teachers teach, and examiners mark scripts, on the basis of what is currently accepted as being true. Science itself is continually changing at its frontiers, and those who work with totally new material cannot appeal to some other authority for a judgement on what is right or not. All they can do is more work, keeping going, until it may become clear that others agree with their results, that their experiments are repeatable, and eventually their work is absorbed into the body of scientific knowledge. Learning science is also a replacement activity, and because some ideas are very strange compared with our everyday experience, it is quite hard, and requires a lot of work right from the beginning. Difficult ideas tend to be introduced in stages, and modified as you go through them. Some people don't like this, thinking that their key stage 4 picture of the atom is in some way a lie, and that the A level view will be too. But the pictures that you get are approximations, which you can build on if you need to or, as I hope you will, want to, as your general scientific and mathematical abilities increase and mature. In many ways your progress through chemical ideas will parallel the way that these ideas have developed historically; your learning of science is similar to the way in which society has learned science – though I hope much faster!

So that we can deal with the real world of experiment, we have to disregard the imperfections which we can ascribe to 'experimental error', but we also have to learn how to know when odd or inconsistent results are the result of some underlying and important feature rather than error. A rather unnerving aspect of chemistry is that apparently small differences in properties, say in energy changes or electron structures, can have large effects on the chemistry which is seen in the test tube.

Although general rules of chemical behaviour are put forward, there are usually exceptions. Thus chemistry needs a broad approach at A level, where many of the exceptions are not considered; if they were, the syllabus would be immense. For this reason, subtle effects are sometimes ignored, but this is done in such a way that if you go on to do chemistry beyond A level, you will not have to unlearn anything.

ATOMIC STRUCTURE

Figure 1.1 John Dalton

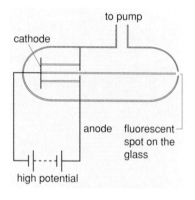

Figure 1.2 The production of cathode rays.

Figure 1.3 Pierre and Marie Curie

Before we start the atomic structure unit, here are some hints. Chemistry is often seen by non-chemists to be a manipulation of formulae on paper, as mysterious, alchemical almost. If you still think this, do the following:

- Imagine yourself as being of atomic or molecular size. This is not easy, but essential to an understanding of what happens to particles as they collide and react.
- Picture in your mind the appearance of the materials that appear in the equations that you write, how they are reacting, the apparatus that you might use. If you don't know some of these things, find out. It is vital that the equations are related to real events; chemistry happens in glassware, not on the pages of a textbook.
- Relate chemistry to everyday life; be aware of the materials you use and why, of the impact of chemistry all around you. After you have studied Topic 4, for example, you should never look at a stained glass window again without thinking of the structure of transition metal ions.

Now for atomic structure. As you work, remember that this material took hundreds of people some 130 years to discover; however you will find out by the end of Topic 3 why you can't pull many everyday objects apart very easily, and yet don't permanently bond to the chair on which you are probably now sitting.

The (much shortened) history

Democritus in 585BC used the word $\alpha\tau o\mu o\zeta$, atom, for the first time. If you read *On the Nature of the Universe* by Lucretius, many of the passages have a familiar ring to them. But the experimental determination of atomic structure, as distinct from the speculative writings of the Greeks, started in 1808 with John Dalton (Figure 1.1). His notion that all substances were made of extremely small, indivisible particles was highly controversial at the time, and there were many highly respected 19th century chemists who did not believe Dalton's hypothesis, even to the ends of their lives.

The investigation of atomic structure got nowhere mainly because of the technological problems. How should the experiments be done? With what tools could the atom be investigated? If you look back over the history of the discovery of the elements, you find that there are spurts of activity that follow a technological advance. Thus the invention of the battery by Volta led rapidly to electrolysis and to the isolation of the alkali and alkaline earth metals. Developments in high-vacuum technology enabled J. Thomson in 1897 to find the ratio of the charge to mass of the cathode rays which were found when a high potential was placed across a gas at low pressure (Figure 1.2), and which had been known about for some time. The particle was shown to be common to all the gases used, and was called the electron.

Similar experiments were performed with the positive particles which were generated in the same experiment by reversing the polarity of the electrodes. The masses of these particles were dependent on the gas in the tube, and Thomson found that the lightest of them came from hydrogen. He called this particle the proton, and he speculated that atoms consisted of a sphere of

2

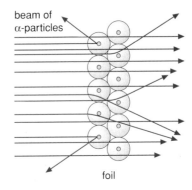

Figure 1.4 The 'gold foil' experiment

protons with electrons embedded in them. This famous 'plum-pudding' model of the atom could not be tested until the tools were available; these came from the Curies.

In 1896 A. H. Becquerel had discovered radioactivity. He had been investigating fluorescence in salts; uranium salts fluoresce strongly, and he had left some in a drawer with a key and a photographic plate wrapped in light-proof wrapping. There was an image of the key on the plate when it was developed, due to the radiation having penetrated through to the plate and so the forming image. Becquerel received the 1903 Nobel Physics prize jointly with Pierre and Marie Curie (Figure 1.3). In 1902 the Curies had taken on the enormous task of isolating the radioactive elements, and produced the first samples of polonium and of radium. Marie died from leukaemia, caused by radiation, in 1934. We now know that radioactivity, X-rays, and many compounds are damaging or fatal, many people having died in the course of their scientific work.

The availability of radium, which emits alpha (α) particles, or helium nuclei, was crucial to the work of Rutherford, Geiger and Marsden who, in the years 1909 to 1911, fired α-particles at metal foils to see how they would be deflected or absorbed (Figure 1.4). If Thomson's model of the atom was correct, the α-particles would have mostly been absorbed, and those which did penetrate the foil would have been deflected only very slightly. This was Rutherford's expectation, since Thomson's atom was very solid. But the majority of the α-particles passed straight through, and a very few bounced back. This so startled Rutherford that he made his now famous assertion that he would have been less surprised if a naval shell had been fired at a sheet of tissue paper and had bounced off. This experiment made possible not only the modern view of the atom, as being essentially mostly empty, but also the measurement of the diameter and charge of the nucleus. Although it is usually called the 'gold foil' experiment, the nuclear size was first estimated for copper and aluminium, in both cases as being about 10^{-14} m.

Rutherford used a foil about 1μm thick for the scattering experiments. The diameter of a gold atom is roughly 3×10^{-10} m. Roughly how many layers of gold atoms did the α-particles pass through?

Investigations in the early 1880s by J. Balmer, a Swiss schoolteacher, on an apparently unrelated matter, were to enable Niels Bohr and his colleagues, some 25 years later, to suggest the way in which electrons are distributed in the atom. Balmer had shown that a gas excited electrically (such as in the sodium street lights with which you are doubtless familiar) gave out light which, when passed through a prism, did not show continuous bands of colour as the rainbow does, but rather than a series of bright lines on a dark background. In the case of hydrogen these lines are quite widely spaced (Figure 1.5 and 1.6).

What sort of force causes the scattering of α-particles by nuclei?

Balmer was able to derive an equation for the frequencies of these lines, but he could not discover the meaning of his results since this required contributions from work which was not carried out until 1900, by Planck.

Bohr's (Figure 1.7) idea was that the lines came about as excited atoms lost their excess energy as light, by falling from high energy levels in the atom to lower ones. The energy levels of the electrons were well-defined, and so therefore were the transitions between them, and this was shown by light of a single frequency, and energy, being emitted for each transition. Bohr was the

Which observation suggests that the nucleus is massive?

ATOMIC STRUCTURE

Figure 1.5 Niels Bohr

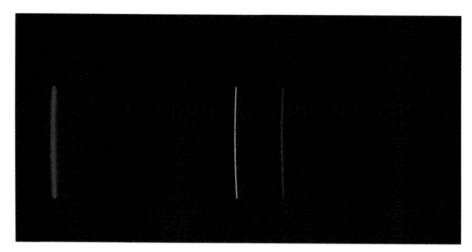

Figure 1.6 Spectrum of excited hydrogen gas

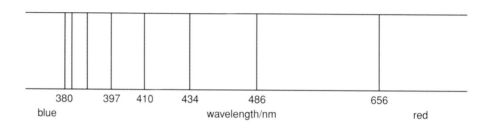

Figure 1.7 The Hydrogen spectrum, or Balmer series

Spectra of atoms with two electrons or more are complex. Species having one electron, such as He$^+$, give simple spectra like that of hydrogen, but the lines have frequencies much higher than those of hydrogen. Can you suggest why?

originator of the shell model of the atom, a sort of miniature solar system, which will be familiar to you. Bohr did not come to this conclusion in isolation, of course; he was able to draw on many other experiments.

The transitions which give rise to the visible spectrum of hydrogen, which is called the *Balmer series* of lines, are shown in Figure 1.8, as well as other series seen in other parts of the spectrum. Further evidence from work on the shell model comes from ionisation energies (discussed later in this chapter).

The energy of a given transition in the hydrogen spectrum is given by E = hf, where h = Planck's constant and f is the frequency of the radiation. What is the energy per atom for the transition giving the red line in the hydrogen spectrum? The frequency of this line is 4.573×10^{14} Hz, and h = 6.262×10^{-34} J s.

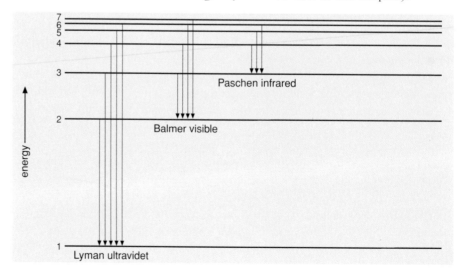

Figure 1.8 Electron transitions in hydrogen

4

Bohr's theory was interesting not least for the fact that he knew when he published it that it had serious imperfections. The main problem was that an orbiting electron is an accelerating charge, and accelerating charges radiate energy. If the electron in an atom did this, it would spiral in to the nucleus, and we would have no atoms. This problem was resolved by Schrödinger and Heisenberg in 1928 when they published their theory of quantum mechanics, considered briefly in the section on atomic orbitals in this chapter.

The last piece of the atomic jigsaw (at least as far as chemistry is concerned) was placed when the neutron was discovered by Chadwick in 1932. It had been known for decades that atoms were more massive than the number of protons in them would allow; that difference in mass was accounted for by the neutrons in the nucleus.

That is not the end of the story of the atom; what is the nucleus like? That is properly a question for physics, and is being actively pursued now. This belongs elsewhere; we must look at the chemical atom in more detail.

Figure 1.9 Erwin Schrödinger

Particles and structure

The particles
The atomic model consists of protons and neutrons in the nucleus, and electrons in shells around the nucleus. The principal properties of these particles are given in Table 1.1.

Table 1.1 *Properties of nuclear particles*

Particle	Mass		Charge	
	Actual/kg	Relative to proton	Actual/C	Relative to proton
proton, p	1.6726×10^{-27}	1	$+1.6 \times 10^{-19}$	+1
neutron, n	1.6750×10^{-27}	just over 1	0	0
electron, e	9.1095×10^{-30}	1/1836	-1.6×10^{-19}	−1

You should have an idea of the relative masses and charges of these particles, but you need not learn their actual values.

The nucleus
The protons and neutrons constitute the nucleus. As the number of protons rises, the number of neutrons increases relatively faster (Figure 1.10), so small atoms have proton and neutron numbers which are comparable, whereas large atoms have many more neutrons than protons. These neutrons act as a sort of diluent, reducing the repulsive forces between the positive protons. The ratio of protons to neutrons is fairly critical, and any departure from the optimum range will lead to nuclear instability and thus radioactivity, which is covered later in this chapter.

The **atomic number** of an element is the number of protons in the nucleus of its atom, and it defines the element. The element with six protons in its nucleus must be carbon. The **mass number** is the number of protons plus the

Suppose you have a nucleus which lies just to the right of the band of stability in Figure 1.10. By which means is it likely to decay?

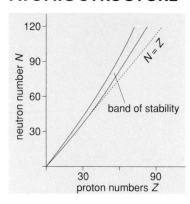

Figure 1.10 *The relation of proton number to neutron number giving stable nuclides*

The atomic number of an element is the number of protons in the nucleus of its atom.
The mass number of the atom is the number of the protons plus the number of neutrons in the nucleus.

Isotopes are atoms having the same atomic number but different mass numbers.

For any element, E,

relative atomic mass =

$$\dfrac{\text{mass of one atom of E}}{1/12 \text{ mass of one atom of carbon-12}}$$

number of neutrons; it is close to, but not identical with, the relative atomic mass, and is always a whole number since you cannot have part of a proton or part of a neutron.

The nucleus constitutes most of the mass of an atom; but the mass of the electrons is not zero. For the majority of practical purposes, however, their mass is ignored.

Isotopes

All atoms have isotopes. The word comes from the Greek for the 'same place', because all the isotopes of a given atom occupy the same place in the Periodic Table defined by the atomic number. Isotopes arise because of changes in the neutron number. This affects the mass of the atom, but it does not affect the electron number or structure, and so does not affect the chemistry of the element. (With isotopes which are significantly different in mass, in practice those of hydrogen, the rates of reaction may vary with the different isotopes, but not the nature of the reaction.) So, isotopes are atoms with the same atomic number but different mass numbers. Some examples of isotopes are mentioned later in this chapter.

The word isotope does not imply radioactivity; carbon has three naturally occurring isotopes, only one of which is radioactive, and four artificial ones which are all radioactive. A nuclear species of a given mass number and atomic number is often called a **nuclide**; radioactive ones are **radionuclides**.

Relative atomic mass

Calculations in chemistry do not need the actual masses of atoms to be known, since they usually involve the relative proportions of the atoms concerned. The **relative atomic mass** is used, where, for historical reasons not important here, the unit of mass is defined as one-twelfth the mass of the carbon-12 isotope, whose mass is defined as 12 units exactly.

The relative molecular mass for a compound (sometimes called the formula mass, especially for ionic substances which have no molecules) is the sum of all the relative atomic masses which make up the compound's formula. Usually the use of masses to 3 significant figures is adequate for A level calculations.

The mass spectrometer

The machine

The mass spectrometer (Figure 1.11) is a device for measuring the masses of positive ions. The mass spectrograph, its forerunner, was invented by F.W. Aston in 1919, for which he received the 1922 Nobel Prize for Chemistry.

Mass spectroscopy makes it possible to determine the structure of compounds by studying the masses of the ions produced by a molecule and the ways in which it fragments or rearranges in the machine.

The essential principles of the mass spectrometer (Figure 1.12) are as follows.

1 Electrons are emitted from the filament, accelerated, and used to bombard the gaseous sample which is at very low pressure.

2 Sample molecules have electrons knocked off them by the bombarding electrons, forming positive ions. The molecule can also fragment and possibly rearrange.

3 The positive ions are accelerated by an electric field.

4 The ions are deflected by a magnetic field in a circular path whose radius depends on their mass/charge ratio and the strength of the field. The machine sweeps over the chosen mass range by altering the magnetic field and hence the ions which reach the detector.

5 The ions are detected, and their relative amounts calculated by the machine.

Figure 1.11 A mass spectrometer

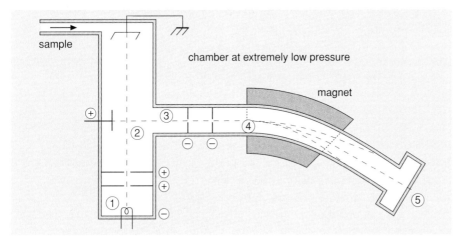

Figure 1.12 Principles of the mass spectrometer

Mass spectra

The mass spectrum is usually converted to a bar graph which shows the relative abundance of the various fragments detected. Because of the variety of fragmentation possible in larger molecules, not all the peaks are interpreted. Practical machines use additional features to ensure that all ions entering the magnetic field have the same energy.

No element in the Periodic table has a relative atomic mass that is a whole number. Why not?

At one time chemists used relative atomic masses based on oxygen = 16, whereas physicists used them based on hydrogen = 1. Why did the two scales not agree?

The electrons are accelerated in the mass spectrometer and pass through holes in the anodes. Why, once the electron has passed the final anode, does it not decelerate and come back to the anode?

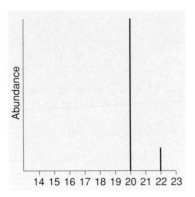

Figure 1.13 *The mass spectrum of neon*

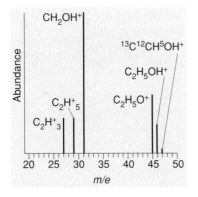

Figure 1.14 *The mass spectum of ethanol*

Why do you think that the likelihood of 2+ ions being produced in the mass spectrometer is very small?

The mass spectrum of zirconium shows peaks at 90 (51.5%), 91 (11.2%), 92 (17.1%), 94 (17.4%), and 96 (2.8%). What is the relative atomic mass of zirconium?

The use of mass spectroscopy enabled the detection of isotopes, and historically, neon was the first element to be so investigated. The relative atomic mass of naturally-occurring elements is not a whole number because it is a weighted mean, and the mass spectrum of neon (Figure 1.13) shows 90.9% of $^{20}Ne^+$, 0.26% of $^{21}Ne^+$, and 8.8% of $^{22}Ne^+$, so the relative atomic mass of the natural material is

$$(0.909 \times 20) + (0.0026 \times 21) + (0.088 \times 22) = 20.17$$

The horizontal axis is strictly mass/charge, m/e.

The mass spectrum of chlorine shows peaks due to Cl^+ and Cl_2^+; two lines from isotopes of masses 35 and 37, and three, from all pairings of these at masses 70, 72, and 74. Knowing the peak heights enables the abundance of each of the isotopes to be calculated. Mass spectroscopy is very accurate; masses are generally quoted as whole numbers, but high-resolution machines can find masses to eight or ten decimal places. The production of singly-positive ions is assumed; the chances of removing two electrons by bombardment to form 2+ ions are very small.

The mass spectroscopy of compounds is more complex, but informative; a simplified spectrum for ethanol is shown in Figure 1.14.

The highest significant peak is usually the molecular ion peak, where the molecule has lost one electron but has not broken up. In this case the peak for $C_2H_5OH^+$ is at $m/e = 46$. (However the molecular ion peak is not always the most intense, and may even be absent.) Carbon-containing compounds give a small peak one unit higher due to the presence of ^{13}C. All the peaks have this accompanying feature, but they are sometimes masked by much larger peaks; this is one reason why mass spectra are often presented in a simplified form.

Fragmentation patterns are useful and characteristic of a given molecule. Peaks in the ethanol spectrum include $C_2H_5O^+$, $m/e = 45$; CH_2OH^+, $m/e = 31$, formed by loss of a methyl group; and $C_2H_5^+$, $m/e = 29$, formed by loss of OH.

Mass spectroscopy is used, together with complementary evidence from other techniques such as infrared (Topic 25, Module 4), ultraviolet and nuclear magnetic resonance spectroscopy, to find the structure of compounds. High resolution machines can distinguish between ions of different composition but which have the same mass on an integer scale.

The mass spectrometer is often coupled with gas–liquid chromatography, especially in forensic work (Figure 1.15), as a very powerful analytical technique for complex mixtures.

Radioactivity

Radioactivity embodies the aim of the alchemists, that is the conversion of one element to another. Unfortunately, though, gold does not figure very much in this. It is a naturally occurring process, all elements having at least one radioactive isotope. Despite the high public profile concerning the uses and abuses of nuclear energy, nuclear activity from this source is only 0.1% of the total daily radiation dose that you receive (Figure 1.16).

Figure 1.15 Mass spectrometry/gas–liquid chromatography in forensic work

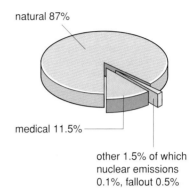

natural 87%

medical 11.5%

other 1.5% of which nuclear emissions 0.1%, fallout 0.5%

Figure 1.16 Total UK radiation exposure

Radioactive decay

Atoms that are radioactive are changing their nuclei, either becoming smaller, or changing the ratio of neutrons to protons, which has to fall within certain bounds if the nucleus is to be stable. There are three types of nuclear decay that we will consider which give rise to three types of radioactivity, alpha (α), beta (β) and gamma (γ) radiation. Their characteristics are shown in Table 1.2, where masses and charges relative to those of the proton are shown.

Table 1.2 *Three types of radioactivity*

Particle	Mass/p	Charge/p	Relative penetration	Speed/m s^{-1}
alpha	4	2	1	10^7
beta	1/1836	−1	100	10^7–10^8
gamma	0	0	10 000	3×10^8

Alpha decay (Figure 1.17)

The α-particle has a double positive charge, a mass of 4 units, and is a helium nucleus. It is given out by large nuclei which are too wobbly to be held together by the force known as the **strong nuclear force**, which is very short range and special to nuclei. All of the elements beyond bismuth, element 83, have isotopes that are α-emitters. The larger the nucleus, the more unstable it is, and the more rapidly the atoms decay. Many of the daughter nuclei will be unstable too, so most large atoms decay in many steps before they become stable, usually finishing up as lead; the thorium decay series (Figure 1.18) is an example.

For a given atom, α-decay produces another atom two places to the left in the periodic table, with a mass number four lower.

Figure 1.17 Decay tracks in a cloud chamber

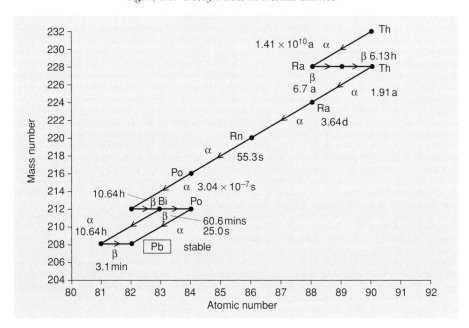

Figure 1.18 The thorium decay series. Most of the decays produce γ-radiation as well

Beta decay

This type of decay is found in nuclei which have too many neutrons for the number of protons, i.e. the n/p ratio is too big. The neutron is converted to a proton and an electron

$$_0^1 n \rightarrow \, _1^1 p + \, _{-1}^0 \beta$$

the electron being emitted. This is the β-particle. The new atom formed is one place to the right in the Periodic Table, but has the same mass number as the original atom.

Gamma emission

This type of radioactivity is generally found with α- or β-decay, and seldom on its own. This is because γ-radiation, which is electrically uncharged, consists of electromagnetic radiation which carries away excess energy from the daughter atom. Sometimes when an α-particle, say, has been lost, the resulting nucleus is still excited and must lose this energy via γ emission (Figure 1.19). Uranium-238 gives two α-particles and one γ, arising from direct decay to the ground-state thorium nucleus, and the intermediate existence of an excited thorium nucleus.

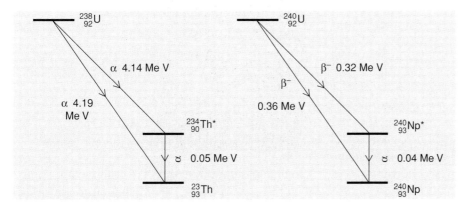

Figure 1.19 *The loss of excess energy in α- and β-decays of $^{238}_{92}U$. 1 MeV = 1.6 × 10^{-13} J*

Ionisation and penetration

All these particles are energetic and leave the atom with considerable speed. Because they are also have high momentum in atomic terms, they can knock electrons out of atoms or molecules with which they collide, and for this reason are called **ionising radiations**. The heaviest, α-radiation, is the most ionising, interacting with matter the most and therefore having the shortest range before it is stopped. It will (depending on its source and hence its energy) usually be stopped by a few centimetres of air, or a sheet of thin paper. Thus α-particles are not particularly dangerous unless their emitters are swallowed or breathed since α-radiation cannot get through clothing. In cells, though, the short range means they are very damaging.

The β-particles cause less ionisation, but have a much greater range. Some of the more energetic β-particles can pass through a few centimetres of lead, and have a considerable range in air. So β-emitters can produce dangerous radiation, even at some distance from the source.

The most penetrating of all are γ-rays, and these will go through many metres of concrete. Their ionising power is the least of all, and many will go through the body without effect. Nevertheless they need treating with great respect, bearing in mind that many α- and β-emitters give γ- too.

Nuclear equations

These, like chemical equations, show the starting material and the product. They may represent decays or nuclear reactions between two starting materials. They must balance for mass and charge. The nuclear charge is indicated at lower left, the mass number at upper left. So for the decay of thorium-232, which is an a-emitter:

$$^{232}_{90}Th \rightarrow ^{228}_{88}Ra + ^{4}_{2}\alpha$$

Suggest a scheme of decay by which $^{214}_{84}Po$ can emit three particles and become its own isotope.

This is the first step in the thorium decay series (Figure 1.18) which includes some β-emissions as well. Most of the decays of atoms of small mass involve β-emissions, some significant ones being:

$$^{14}_{6}C \rightarrow {}^{14}_{7}N + {}^{0}_{-1}\beta$$

$$^{32}_{15}P \rightarrow {}^{32}_{16}S + {}^{0}_{-1}\beta$$

$$^{90}_{38}Sr \rightarrow {}^{90}_{39}Y + {}^{0}_{-1}\beta$$

Uses of radioactive decay

Carbon-14, whose decay is represented in the first of the above three equations, exists in all living systems. It is produced in the upper atmosphere by cosmic ray bombardment of nitrogen, and since carbon-14 takes a long time to decay organisms come into equilibrium with it as $^{14}CO_2$ is incorporated into food via photosynthesis. When the organism dies, this equilibrium ceases, and the carbon-14 decays. By comparison with present $^{12}C/^{14}C$ ratios, the ratio of $^{12}C/^{14}C$ in the dead material will enable an estimate of its age to be made.

Phosphorus-32 has been used in tracer experiment to determine the fate of phosphate, PO_4^{3-}, taken up by plants. The path of the radioactivity through the plant is traced using autoradiography, where the tissues are placed on a photographic emulsion, and the position of the radioactivity is found by the darkening of the film.

The last of the decays shown was of particular interest in the 1950s when the UK, USA and USSR were testing nuclear weapons in the atmosphere., Strontium-90 was part of the fallout, and was found in milk. The body cannot tell the difference between strontium and calcium, so there was much concern at the time about the effect of this damaging radioactive species on bone.

Nuclear reactions

Nuclear reactions, in contrast to spontaneous decay, involve bombarding some target material with other particles or atoms at high energies, in order to generate new nuclei. All the known elements beyond uranium, 92, have been produced by such reactions. The first nuclear reaction was carried out by Rutherford in 1919:

$$^{14}_{7}N + {}^{4}_{2}He \rightarrow {}^{17}_{8}O + {}^{1}_{1}H$$

The neutron was discovered by James Chadwick at Cambridge in 1932 as a result of another nuclear reaction:

$$^{9}_{4}Be + {}^{4}_{2}He \rightarrow {}^{12}_{6}C + {}^{1}_{0}n$$

The reaction which enables uranium to be used for nuclear fuel or weapons according to the rate of reaction (Figure 1.20) is that where neutrons emitted from the breakdown of one uranium nucleus bombard other uranium nuclei and induce them to decay too. It's an example of a **branching chain reaction**, where more particles (neutrons), which are involved in succeeding

Explain why, when a small quantity of radium is enclosed with nitrogen in a sealed tube, traces of hydrogen appear.

Complete the following reactions:

$$^{35}_{17}Cl + {}^{1}_{0}n \rightarrow {}^{36}_{17}Cl + \ldots$$

$$^{32}_{16}S + {}^{1}_{0}n \rightarrow {}^{1}_{1}p + \ldots$$

$$^{6}_{3}Li + {}^{1}_{0}n \rightarrow {}^{4}_{2}He + \ldots$$

stages, are produced than are used up. Branching chain reactions usually give an explosive increase in rate, which is why there are such complicated control devices and procedures for nuclear power stations. One possible reaction (not the only one) is

$$^{235}_{92}U + ^{1}_{0}n \rightarrow ^{94}_{38}Sr + ^{139}_{54}Xe + 2^{1}_{0}n$$

Nuclear fusion

A potentially very important type of reaction is nuclear fusion, where two small nuclei are brought together at very high temperature to make heavier nuclei. This is an energy-releasing reaction if the starting nuclei are small, one process being

$$^{2}H + ^{2}H = ^{4}He$$

which is fairly easy to perform as an explosion – it is the hydrogen bomb – but which has been very difficult to arrange in a controlled manner. The problem is the containment of ionised gas at temperatures of around $10^9\,$K for long enough to let fusion happen. The JET project at Culham in Oxfordshire (Figure 1.21) is a multinational effort to achieve controllable fusion. The energy output happens because the product nuclide is slightly less massive than the reacting nuclides. The amount of energy released is given by one of the most famous equations ever written:

$$E = \Delta mc^2$$

where Δm is the mass difference between the two sides of the equation and c is the speed of light. Fusion is an attractive power source since there is relatively little radioactive waste produced, and the fuel, hydrogen, is present in virtually unlimited supply.

The energy released by fusion is a result of the product nuclei having a smaller mass than the starting nuclei. Given the following masses, find the energy released when 2g of deuterium fuses with 3g of tritium, assuming complete conversion to helium in the reaction

$$^{3}_{1}H + ^{2}_{1}H \rightarrow ^{1}_{0}n + ^{4}_{2}He$$

Masses/10^{-27}kg:

$^{3}_{1}$H 5.00656, $^{4}_{2}$He 0.64432, $^{2}_{1}$H 3.34341, $^{1}_{0}$n 1.67444

speed of light c = 3×10^8m s^{-1}; Avogadro constant = 6.022×10^{23}mol^{-1}

Half-life

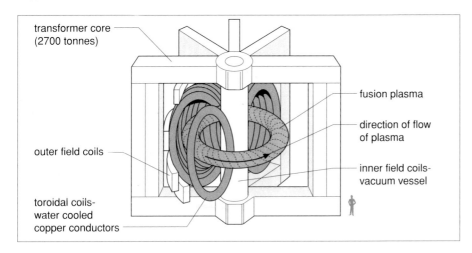

Figure 1.21 The joint European Torus (JET) project

The half-life of an element is the time taken for half the number of its atoms present at some arbitrary initial time to decay.

The half-life of an element is the time taken for half the number of its atoms present at some arbitrary initial time to decay. It is independent of the initial number of atoms, so the time taken for 1 kg of uranium to decay to 0.5 kg is

The half-life of C is 5730a. If a sample of linen (made from flax) has 78% of the amount of ^{14}C that present-day flax has, how long ago was the linen woven? What is the principal assumption in radio carbon dating?

A sample of iodine-128 shows the following activity at various times. Find the half-life for ^{128}I decay.

t/min	20	40	60
counts /s^{-1}	6375	3640	2100
t/min	80	100	120
counts /s^{-1}	1190	665	385

The activity of a sample of ^{35}S falls to 25% of its initial value after 174 days. What is its half-life? What percentage will remain after 10 half-lives have elapsed?

the same as 0.5kg takes to decay to 0.25kg. (The number of atoms is proportional to the mass of the uranium.) This type of decay is called **exponential**. It is a statistical measure, so it is meaningless to talk about the half life of a single atom which may decay in the next 10 milliseconds or may remain intact for ever. The half-life depends on the particular nucleus, the more unstable it is the shorter the half-life.

This does not mean that a chunk of uranium will have halved in mass after one half-life, since the daughter nuclei are solids as well. It just means that the number of uranium atoms will have halved.

The range of half-lives is very great. Look at ^{6}Be and ^{238}U in Table 1.3, for example. Even those for different radioactive isotopes of the same element can vary enormously, eg for ^{14}C and ^{16}C, or, more dramatically, ^{8}Be and ^{10}Be.

The amount of a radioactive species at some future time can be predicted from the half life: the fraction of atoms remaining after x half-lives is $(1/2)^x$; so if N_o is the initial number of atoms, the number N after x half-lives is

$$N = N_o(1/2)^x$$

This equation enables the prediction of the useful lifetime of a radioactive element used in industry or medicine, where the activity needs to be accurately known.

Table 1.3 *Half-lives of some nuclides*

Nuclide	Half-life
$^3_1$H	12.26 a (years)
$^6_4$Be	4×10^{-21} s
$^7_4$Be	53 d
$^8_4$Be	2×10^{-16} s
$^{10}_4$Be	2.5×10^6 a
$^{11}_4$Be	13.6 s
$^{10}_6$C	19 s
$^{11}_6$C	20.3 min
$^{12}_6$C	stable
$^{13}_6$C	stable
$^{14}_6$C	5730 a
$^{15}_6$C	2.4 s
$^{16}_6$C	0.74 s
$^{235}_{92}$U	7.1×10^8 a
$^{238}_{92}$U	4.51×10^9 a

Uses of radioactive isotopes

Apart from nuclear power, radio-isotopes are used widely in industry, medicine and research.Some of these uses include the following.

- Measurement of the thickness of metals from sheet rolling mills. A source is placed on one side of the sheet and a detector on the other. The use of a long-lived nuclide enables the consistency of the thickness of the metal to be monitored via the constancy of the count-rate.
- Use in radiotherapy machines (Figure 1.22). Cobalt-60 is commonly used for the treatment of cancers. Many tumour cells are more sensitive to radiation than is healthy tissue, and they can therefore be treated using radiation of suitable energy. There are some drugs which make the tumour even more sensitive, and can reduce damage to the surrounding tissue by reducing the required dose.
- Use in tracer experiments. Since radionuclides have the same chemical properties as their stable isotopes, the path of molecules labelled with a suitable nuclide can be traced through reactions or metabolic processes in organisms by following the radioactivity. A widely-used isotope in biochemistry is carbon-14, and the use of phosphorus-32 has been mentioned earlier. Sometimes short-lived isotopes are used in clinical medicine for diagnosis.

Radioactive sources are often used to ensure that welds, for example on pipelines, are uniform and free from flaws. The source is pulled through the pipe; how do you think the uniformity of the weld might be checked?

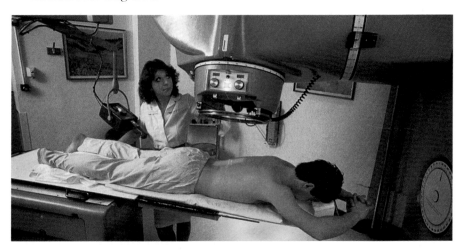

Figure 1.22 A radiotherapy machine

Ionisation energy

Further evidence for the existence of electrons in shells comes from a study of the ionisation energies of atoms

Successive ionisation energies increase because the electrons are being removed from increasingly positive ions and so the attractive forces are greater. There are large jumps in ionisation energies arising from a large increase in attraction for the removed electron, which correspond to the electron being removed from a new energy level significantly closer to the nucleus. Figure 1.23 shows the successive ionisation energies for sodium. These energies show the electron structure of the atom; for sodium there are clearly three shells, with one electron in the outermost, a jump to the next shell with eight electrons, and then a larger one (because the positive charge from the nucleus is now much stronger) to remove the final two.

The first ionisation energy is the amount of energy required per mole to remove an electron from each atom in the gas phase to form a singly positive ion, that is

$$M(g) = M^+(g) + e^-$$

The second ionisation energy is defined as the energy per mole for:

$$M^+(g) = M^{2+}(g) + e^-$$

and so on for successive ionisation energies.

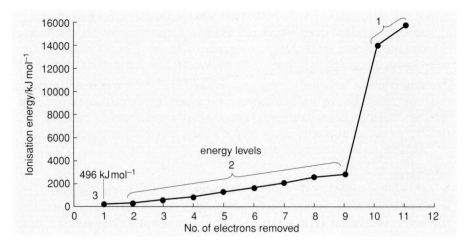

Figure 1.23 Successive ionisation energies for sodium

Ionisation energy and the periodic table

Ionisation energies are important not only as evidence for energy levels, but also in determining the type of bonds which an element will form. This is dealt with fully in Topic 3 of this book, but we must consider here the way in which ionisation energies change across the periodic table. The first ionisation energies for elements up to krypton, element 36, are plotted against atomic number in Figure 1.25.

Using a data book plot the logarithm of the successive ionisation energies of sodium vs the number of the electrons removed. Why do you think this plot is often preferred to that of Figure 1.23? Can you see any disadvantage in doing it?

Write the equation which represents the fifth ionisation of sodium.

Sodium ions are smaller than sodium atoms; chloride ions are larger than chlorine atoms; sodium atoms are larger than chlorine atoms, but sodium ions are smaller than chloride ions. Why?

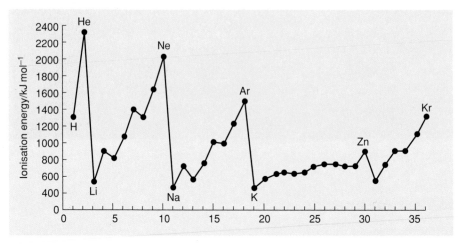

Figure 1.24 The first ionisation energies (in kJ mol⁻¹) of the elements up to krypton

The repetition of the general pattern up to element 20 is clear. The highest points are the noble gases in group 0, the lowest ones the alkali metals. Hydrogen is quite high at 1312 kJ mol^{-1}, and its ion is never found as such in compounds; it is invariably bonded with something else, for example water in aqueous acids to form the hydroxonium ion H_3O^+, the energy released in this process compensating for the ionisation energy.

The low values for the alkali metals mean that the ionisation energy is compensated by the electron affinity of the non-metal with which they react and the lattice enthalpy of the resulting compound; almost their whole chemistry is that of ionic compounds. The halogens in group 7 have rather high ionisation energies, so they do not form positive ions. Instead they form negative ones (see page 30, *Electron affinity*).

The falls between beryllium (atomic number 4) and boron (5), and nitrogen (7) and oxygen (8), give further detail about the electronic structures. From the spectra, and the successive ionisation energies of a given atom, we know that the electrons are arranged in shells. These are simply numbered 1, 2, and so on from the nucleus out. But the picture of ionisation energy from lithium to neon (atomic numbers 3 to 10) shows the existence of subshells within the shells. There seems to be some significance concerning the elements grouped as a pair, lithium and beryllium, and two triplets; boron, carbon, nitrogen and oxygen, fluorine, neon. The full story of the discovery of the subshells is complex and not appropriate here, but in the second shell there are two subshells called the s and p; in the third shell there are three, the s, p and d. The subshells of a given shell are quite close together in energy. The s subshell can contain two electrons, the p six, and the d ten. The first shell has no subshell. So the shells and subshells up to the fourth shell (which also has an 'f' subshell) can contain the following number of electrons:

subshell	1s	2s 2p	3s 3p 3d	4s 4p 4d 4f
maximum number of electrons	2	2 6	2 6 10	2 6 10 14

There is now a further layer to the atomic onion. Each subshell has further divisions, one in the s subshell, three in the p subshell and five in the d. (You will have noticed that this is half the number of permissible electrons.) These sub-subshells are called *orbitals*, and their nature is considered further later in this chapter.

The 'aufbau' principle

Although these arrangements arose from the mathematical theory of atomic structure, it is enough for your purposes to think of the subshells as boxes into which atoms put electrons. So we'll see how the electrons are arranged in these boxes. The 'aufbau' or 'build-up' principle enables the prediction of the electronic structure of an atom. Electrons are added to the lowest energy orbital available, one at a time, with no more than two electrons occupying any one orbital. If there are several orbitals of the same energy available (for example there are three p orbitals) then electrons enter these orbitals singly so as to be as far apart as possible.

The order of filling which results is shown in Figure 1.25. It can be justified from the mathematical theory of the atom.

Let us consider the electronic structures for the first 21 elements, and see how they relate to the structure of the periodic table and to the ionisation energy graph of Figure 1.13. Using the idea of electrons in boxes, hydrogen and helium are easy; electrons go into the 1s shell.

H   1s [| |]   He   1s [| |]

Use a data book to obtain values for the first and second ionisation energies of the elements up to Krypton. Plot these values on the same axes. Explain the relationship of the second ionisation energy graph to that for the first.

Using a data book plot the first ionisation energies of the alkali metals, group 1, vs atomic number. Plot the metallic radius vs atomic number for the same group, and comment on the relationship between the two graphs.

The ionisation energy of hydrogen can be found from its spectrum; so can that of hydrogen-like (one-electron) species such as Li^{2+}. The spectral lines converge to a limit, which corresponds via $E = hf$ to the ionisation energy. Plot the following frequencies of the spectral lines of Li^{2+} vs the number of the transition, and extrapolate the graph to get a value for the convergence limit. Evaluate the energy required for the process

$$Li^{2+}(g) \rightarrow Li^{3+}(g) + e^-.$$

Frequencies/10^{14}Hz: 2.20 2.63 2.77 2.84 2.88 2.90

Planck's constant
$h = 6.6262 \times 10^{-34}$ J s.

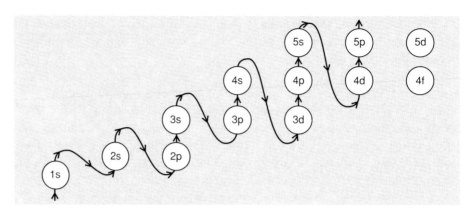

Figure 1.25 The order of filling of atomic orbitals.

The 1s is now full; it is very difficult to remove electrons from full shells , so the ionisation energy of helium is high. The next electron must go in to the 2s subshell, according to our picture, so lithium is

This can also be written $1s^2 2s^1$. The lone electron is quite easy to remove; a full shell is not being broken, and the 3+ charge on the lithium nucleus is to some extent shielded from the outer electron by the inner electrons, so the outer electron is held by an effective nuclear charge which is rather less than three (actually about +1.3). With beryllium, the next electron also goes into the 2s giving: $1s^2 2s^2$. The 2s subshell is now full, so in the boron atom the 2p subshell starts to fill, giving $1s^2 2s^2 2p^1$. The 2p electron, somewhat on its own, is slightly easier to remove than is the 2s electron from B, because subshells that are full are somewhat more stable than those which are not. Carbon has the electron structure $1s^2 2s^2 2p^2$, and nitrogen $1s^2 2s^2 2p^3$.

Oxygen is $1s^2 2s^2 2p^4$; in boxes, and with the orbitals shown, we have

and it's not hard to see that the final electron will be repelled a little since it is paired up in a 2p orbital, so it is a bit easier to remove. Neon is $1s^2 2s^2 2p^6$, and the second shell is now full.

The periodic table is arranged according to electron structure; there are two groups, 1 and 2, where the outer electrons are s electrons, so this is called the **s-block**. There are six groups where the p orbitals are filling, and this **p-block** forms groups 3 to 0.

The aufbau principle shows that the fourth shell starts to fill (the 4s subshell) before the third shell is complete. This finishes filling with elements 21–30 (corresponding rows fill the 4d and 5d subshells); this block is the **d-block**.

The ionisation energies of the d-block metals do not change nearly as markedly as those of the main groups. This is because along the first transition series electrons are being added to an inner shell (below) and the effect of increased nuclear charge is more or less compensated by these added electrons. So the sizes of the d-block elements do not change enormously, and neither do their ionisation energies.

Table 1.4 *Electronic structures of the first 36 elements*

Atomic number	symbol	1s	2s	2p	3s	3p	3d	4s	4p
1	H	1							
2	He	2							
3	Li	2	1						
4	Be	2	2						
5	B	2	2	1					
6	C	2	2	2					
7	N	2	2	3					
8	O	2	2	4					
9	F	2	2	5					
10	Ne	2	2	6					
11	Na	2	2	6	1				
12	Mg	2	2	6	2				
13	Al	2	2	6	2	1			
14	Si	2	2	6	2	2			
15	P	2	2	6	2	3			
16	S	2	2	6	2	4			
17	Cl	2	2	6	2	5			
18	Ar	2	2	6	2	6			
19	K	2	2	6	2	6		1	
20	Ca	2	2	6	2	6		2	
21	Sc	2	2	6	2	6	1	2	
22	Ti	2	2	6	2	6	2	2	
23	V	2	2	6	2	6	3	2	
24	Cr	2	2	6	2	6	5	1	
25	Mn	2	2	6	2	6	5	2	
26	Fe	2	2	6	2	6	6	2	
27	Co	2	2	6	2	6	7	2	
28	Ni	2	2	6	2	6	8	2	
29	Cu	2	2	6	2	6	10	1	
30	Zn	2	2	6	2	6	10	2	
31	Ga	2	2	6	2	6	10	2	1
32	Ge	2	2	6	2	6	10	2	2
33	As	2	2	6	2	6	10	2	3
34	Se	2	2	6	2	6	10	2	4
35	Br	2	2	6	2	6	10	2	5
36	Kr	2	2	6	2	6	10	2	6

ATOMIC STRUCTURE

Write the electronic configurations of the following elements, both in 1s 2s 2p . . . notation and as electrons-in-boxes: $_9$F, $_{14}$Si, $_{21}$Sc, $_{31}$Ga.

The electronic configuration of the elements up to krypton is shown in Table 1.4. Since they can get quite long, electronic configurations are shown in abbreviated form, where the symbol of the nearest inert gas of lower atomic mass than the element of interest, is shown in square brackets; thus potassium could be written $[Ar]4s^1$.

The electronic structure is central to the chemistry of an element; the number of the electrons in the outer (valence) shell and, in some cases the shell next to the outer shell, together with the ionisation and electron gain energies for an atom, will determine the chemistry of the element.

Atomic orbitals

We have already mentioned that the orbiting electron model of the atom was known to be in error when Bohr proposed it. The solution of this problem came in 1928, when Schrodinger and others developed quantum mechanics, which amongst other things said that the electron in an atom behaves as if it is a wave, not a particle. This is a difficult idea, and its development does not belong here, but instead of orbiting electrons we have the **atomic orbital**. This is a volume of space, often of strange shape, which is occupied by up to two electrons themselves. This is how it is often described; in fact the orbital *is* the electron or pair of electrons. Don't try to visualise an electron turning into a wave, or existing simultaneously as a wave and a particle. In any case this wave is a mathematical construction, not a wave actually in anything. Instead, the orbital can be seen as either the volume in which the electron has a 95% probability of being found; or, in a much looser but quite useful way, a volume of space which has a property which might be called 'electron-ness', that is a volume within which the electron can behave as electrons do. Principally this is in formation of bonds, which form by the overlap of orbitals thus increasing the electron density between the bonded atoms. This is covered in detail in Topic 3.

The shapes of the atomic orbitals for hydrogen are shown in Figure 1.26. The orbitals are assumed to be the same shape for other atoms. This is necessary

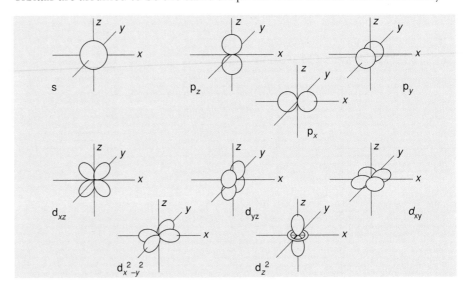

Figure 1.26 Hydrogen atomic orbitals

because exact calculation for atoms with more than one electron is not at present possible, since the mathematical techniques do not exist. When we come to bonding we will sometimes talk of empty orbitals; this is a convenience, as you will see, but since the orbital is the electron, there is really no such thing as an empty orbital.

Electron affinity

The electron affinity is important when deciding what sort of bonding non-metals should show, and is considered further in Topic 3. Some values (in $kJ\,mol^{-1}$) are given in Table 1.5.

The second electron affinity is positive, because in the reaction

$$X^-(g) + e^- \rightarrow X^{2-}(g)$$

an electron is being added to an ion which is already negative, and there is repulsion between the similar charges.

Table 1.5 *Some electron affinities*

Species	Electron affinity/$kJ\,mol^{-1}$
H	−72.8
C	−122.3
O	−141.1
O⁻	about 798
F	−328.0
P	−328.0
S	−200.4
S⁻	640.0
Cl	−348.8
Br	−324.6
I	−295.4

The electron affinity, also called the electron gain energy, is defined as the energy change per mole for

$X(g) + e^- = X^-(g)$

that is for the acquisition of electrons by gaseous atoms to form anions in the gas phase.

Plot the values of (a) covalent radius, (b) ionisation energy, (c) electron affinity, vs atomic number for the halogens, group 7. Use small graphs. Make any comments you can about the relationship between these graphs.

2 Quantitative chemistry

The ability to calculate is central to all physical sciences; a hypothesis may look delightful whilst stated in qualitative terms, but the acid test is always whether the quantitative predictions that have been made stand up to examination. Calculations occur throughout chemistry, but in this topic only reacting masses and volumes are considered, together with the use of chemical equations to represent reactions.

When solving calculation problems you should always aim to understand what is going on rather than relying on formulae learned by rote, which are easily mis-remembered or applied wrongly, and you should do as many examples as you can.

The types of calculation outlined here can be part of a test question for any of the modules, using the syllabus material in that module.

Empirical and molecular formulae

Chemists write equations for several reasons.
- They are internationally understood. A chemistry paper written anywhere in the world in any alphabet system will have recognisable equations in it.
- They are quantitative; they tell you not only which substances are involved, but how much of each.
- They are shorter than the same information given in words. The 'word equation' is not an equation at all because it is not quantitative.

Equations contain formulae, and formulae are calculated from analytical data. When a new compound is made, it will be analysed to see how much of each element is present in it. This is now done by machine (Figure 2.1) rather than by the lengthy methods necessary in the past, but you have to know how to find the empirical formula from the results.

Figure 2.1 An auto-analyser used to determine the empirical formulae of compounds

The **empirical formula** shows the ratio of atoms present in their lowest terms, i.e. smallest numbers. Any compound having one hydrogen atom for every carbon atom will have the empirical formula CH; calculation of the **molecular formula** will need extra information, since ethyne, C_2H_2, cyclobutadiene, C_4H_4, and benzene, C_6H_6, all have CH as their empirical formula.

As an example we shall use the compound having the composition by mass 52.18% carbon, 13.04% hydrogen, and 34.78% oxygen. When finding the numbers of each atom, the different masses of the atoms must be considered. The percentage by mass is therefore divided by the relative atomic mass, i.e. 12 for carbon, 1 for hydrogen and 16 for oxygen, giving:

$$C_{\frac{52.18}{12}}H_{\frac{13.04}{1}}O_{\frac{34.78}{16}} = C_{4.35}H_{13.04}O_{2.17}$$

These numbers are now divided by the smallest to get whole-number ratios:

$$C_{\frac{4.35}{2.17}}H_{\frac{13.04}{2.17}}O_{\frac{2.17}{2.17}} = C_2H_6O, \text{ which is the empirical formula.}$$

Occasionally, mostly in substances containing only two atoms, this process does not give entirely whole number answers. So the compound containing 82.76% C and 17.24% H by mass gives $CH_{2.5}$ as its empirical formula by the method above. In this case, multiply by 2 to get C_2H_5 which is the empirical formula. If such multiplication is needed, it will always be by a small whole number.

In order to get the molecular formula you need to know something else about the compound other than its percentage composition by mass. Commonly the relative molecular mass is given. For example: 92.31% carbon and 7.69% hydrogen gives empirical formula CH, which has a relative mass of 13. If the compound has a relative molecular mass of 78, the number of CH units in each molecule is 78/13, or six. The molecule is therefore C_6H_6.

You could be given other information to convert the empirical into the molecular formula. If you find the empirical formula for 26.67% carbon, 71.11% oxygen, 2.22 % hydrogen, you will get CO_2H. If you are told that the substance is a dibasic acid, that is one which has two replaceable hydrogen atoms per molecule, it makes the molecular formula $C_2H_2O_4$.

Equations

You cannot avoid equations in chemistry! So use every opportunity you have to practise them, and if you cannot work them out look them up; the use of reference materials such as other textbooks or data books or journals is in any case an important part of learning how to learn. You should make the resolutions to: *never refer to any reaction in anything you write unless you give the equation for it*, and *never refer to a compound (or indeed read about one) without learning its formula*. Formulae and equations are the vocabulary and grammar of chemistry, and it is impossible to know too many.

A compound contains C 62.08%, H 10.34%, O 27.58% by mass. Find its empirical formula and its molecular formula given that its molar mass is 58g mol⁻¹.

A compound contains H 1.75%, S 28.08%, O 70.17% by mass. Find its empirical formula. Given that this is also its molecular formula, write the equation for its reaction with aqueous sodium hydroxide.

Find the empirical formula of the compound containing C 22.02%, H 4.59%, Br 73.39% by mass.

A compound containing 85.71% C and 14.29% H by mass has a relative molecular mass of 56. Find its molecular formula.

It is pointless to give lots of examples here, since there are equations scattered throughout the book. The following principles always apply:

1 Equations balance for mass, so the left and right-hand sides have the same number of each type of atom. If equations need balancing, for example

$$Fe(s) + Cl_2(g) \rightarrow FeCl_3(s)$$

you cannot change the formulae. Balancing must be done by altering only the number in front of the formula, i.e.

$$2Fe(s) + 3Cl_2(g) \rightarrow 2FeCl_3(s)$$

2 Equations must balance for total charge; if there are two positives on the left, there must be two on the right. These could come from any combination of charges, as long as the total charge is the same.

Ionic equations

Ionic equations are often used in inorganic chemistry to reduce the amount of unnecessary information and highlight the processes taking place. To turn an ordinary equation into an ionic one, you
1 Write all soluble ionic compounds with the ions separated.
2 Write all insoluble ionic compounds and all covalent compounds in the usual manner.
3 Cross out ions which appear on both sides of the equation. These are called **spectator ions**, since they are sitting there while things happen around them.

An example is the reaction between sodium chloride and silver nitrate, both soluble, to give insoluble silver chloride and soluble sodium nitrate:

$$NaCl(aq) + AgNO_3(aq) \rightarrow NaNO_3(aq) + AgCl(s)$$

Writing down the ions, we have

$$Na^+(aq) + Cl^-(aq) + Ag^+(aq) + NO_3^-(aq) \rightarrow Na^+(aq) + NO_3^-(aq) + AgCl(s)$$

Deleting the common ions from both sides, we get the ionic equation for the reaction:

$$Ag^+(aq) + Cl^-(aq) \rightarrow AgCl(s)$$

No information that matters has been lost, since the interest lies in the precipitation of the silver chloride, not the ions that are left over.

In some cases the simplification is considerable; thus in the reaction between iron(II) sulphate and potassium manganate(VII) in the presence of sulphuric acid, the full equation is

$$2KMnO_4(aq) + 8H_2SO_4(aq) + 10FeSO_4(aq) \rightarrow$$

$$2MnSO_4(aq) + 5Fe_2(SO_4)_3(aq) + K_2SO_4(aq) + 8H_2O(l)$$

whereas the ionic equation is

$$MnO_4^-(aq) + 8H^+(aq) + 5Fe^{2+}(aq) \rightarrow Mn^{2+}(aq) + 5Fe^{3+}(aq) + 4H_2O(l)$$

State symbols should be included, since they help you to visualise the reaction taking place.

Reacting masses

The Avogadro constant and the mole

Equations enable one to calculate how much material to use to get a desired amount of product, whatever the scale. The essential link between the equation and the quantities of material you weigh out is the mole.

Suppose the reaction of interest is

$$Fe(s) + S(s) \rightarrow FeS(s).$$

Iron and sulphur react on heating to give iron(II) sulphide, which is a hard, dark-grey solid. The equation tells us that one atom of iron reacts with one of sulphur; and we know from tables of relative atomic masses that iron has a relative atomic mass of 56 and sulphur 32. One atom of each cannot be weighed, but since the elements react in the ratio of 56 parts of iron to 32 parts of sulphur by mass, we could use 56 g of iron and 32 g of sulphur which we can weigh out. Further, since these large masses are in the same ratio as the masses of the atoms, 56 g of iron and 32 g of sulphur contain the same number of atoms.

This number of atoms is called the Avogadro constant, N_A, after the Italian chemist Amadeo Avogadro, who in 1811 stated that equal volumes of all gases under the same conditions contain the same number of particles. Its value is 6.02×10^{23} mol^{-1}, and this number of particles defines the amount of substance called the **mole**. One mole of any substance is 6.02×10^{23} particles of it, which may be molecules or ions or atoms, depending on the substance. Such an enormous number of particles cannot be counted, but can be weighed; a mole of iron is 56 g, and that of sulphur is 32 g. A mole of any substance is that substance's atomic or molecular mass expressed in grams, and this mass is called the **molar mass**. Unlike relative atomic or molecular masses, it has units. The **number of moles of any substance** is the **amount** of it. The word 'amount' is used in a technical sense in chemistry, with a precise meaning.

There is nothing fundamental about the Avogadro constant, since its magnitude depends on the mass units which are chosen to measure the molar mass. Had pounds (lbs) been chosen, N_A would be 454 times as big (454 g = 1 lb). The magnitude of N_A was first found by the German chemist Loschmidt, and in Europe it is often called Loschmidt's number. Its value is seldom needed, but the idea, summarised below, lies at the bottom of every reacting mass calculation. (The values of physical constants, and relative atomic masses, will always be given in any examination.)

The Avogadro constant, N_A, is 6.02×10^{23} mol^{-1}. One mol of any substance is 6.02×10^{23} particles of it; depending on the substance these particles may be molecules, ions or atoms. One mol of any substance is its relative molecular or relative atomic mass expressed in grams; this is also called the molar mass. (The SI symbol for the Avogadro constant is L.)

$$Fe(s) \quad + \quad S(s) \quad \rightarrow \quad FeS(s)$$

1 atom	1 atom	1 molecule
56	32	88

$\times N_A$ $\times N_A$ $\times N_A$

1 mole	1 mole	1 mole
56g	32g	88g

Reacting masses

Now that you have the idea of the mole, and can see the relationship of masses of substances to the numbers of atoms or molecules involved, calculation of the amounts of any of the substances is simply an exercise in proportion, if the amount of one of them is known. The amount can then be converted into the mass.

Refer again to the iron–sulphur reaction. All calculation is done in terms of numbers of moles, that is, the amount, where

$$\text{number of moles} = \frac{\text{mass of substance}}{\text{molar mass}}$$

Suppose 5.6 g of iron was used; how much sulphur is needed, and how much iron (II) sulphide is produced? The calculation is as follows:

$$Fe(s) + S(s) = FeS(s)$$

$$\text{no of moles of iron} = \frac{5.6}{56}$$

$$= 0.1$$

The number of moles of sulphur and iron (II) sulphide is the same as that of the iron, according to the equation. The mass of each substance then, is equal to the number of moles times the molar mass of that substance:

	Fe(s) +	S(s) →	FeS(s)
mol	0.1	0.1	0.1
mass		0.1×32	0.1×88
		= 3.2 g	= 8.8 g

Suppose that 0.82 g of iron had been used at first.

	Fe(s) +	S(s)	=	FeS(s)
mol	$\frac{0.82}{56}$			
	= 0.0146			

mass		0.0146 × 32	0.0146 × 88
		= 0.467g	= 1.285g

When copper (II) nitrate is heated, it decomposes according to:

$2Cu(NO_3)_2(s) \rightarrow 2CuO(s) + 4NO_2(g) + O_2(g)$

When 20.0g of copper (II) nitrate is decomposed what mass of copper (II) oxide would be produced? If this CuO is converted to copper, how much would be produced?

What mass of sulphur is required to make 1 tonne (1000kg) of sulphuric acid H_2SO_4?

Consider now a calculation where the proportions reacting are not 1:1. The reaction of sodium carbonate with hydrochloric acid is

$$Na_2CO_3(s) + 2HCl(aq) \rightarrow 2NaCl(aq) + H_2O(l) + CO_2(g).$$

To find the masses involved the molar masses of the compounds must be found. It is a good idea to write out the addition in full; if this is not done, it is impossible for your teacher or examiner to tell whether errors are chemical or arithmetical. For each substance in the reaction, then

Na_2CO_3: $(2 \times 23) + 12 + (3 \times 16) = 46 + 12 + 48 = 106\,g\,mol^{-1}$

HCl: $1 + 35.5 = 36.5\,g\,mol^{-1}$

$NaCl$: $23 + 35.5 = 58.5\,g\,mol^{-1}$

H_2O: $(2 \times 1) + 16 = 18\,g\,mol^{-1}$

CO_2: $12 + (2 \times 16) = 44\,g\,mol^{-1}$

Suppose we are to find the various masses that react with or are produced from 7.3 g of sodium carbonate.

$$Na_2CO_3(s) + 2HCl(aq) \rightarrow 2NaCl(aq) + H_2O(l) + CO_2(g)$$

mol $\frac{7.3}{106}$

= 0.069   0.138   0.138   0.069   0.069

mass 0.138×36.5 = 5.03 g 0.138×58.5 = 8.06 g 0.069×18 = 1.24 g 0.069×44 = 3.03 g

Use of concentrations: volumetric analysis

Much quantitative analysis is performed using reactions between two substances in solution, the volumes of both solutions and the concentration of one of them being accurately known when the reaction is complete. The concentration of the other solution can then be found. This technique is **volumetric analysis**, or **titration**.

Remember, do not rely on mathematical formulae. Instead work in moles, and be aware of what you are doing.

Solution concentrations are usually given in mol dm^{-3} or g dm^{-3}, in both cases the "dm^{-3}" referring to the *solution*, and not to the added solvent. To make a molar solution of a substance, one mole of it is weighed out, and water added until the volume of the solution is 1 dm^3.

Acid/base titrations

In these titrations acid and base are reacted in the presence of a suitable indicator.

Lead (IV) oxide reacts with concentrated hydrochloric acid thus:

$$PbO_2(s) + 4HCl(aq) \rightarrow PbCl_2(s) + Cl_2(g) + 2H_2O$$

What mass of lead chloride would be obtained from 37.2g of PbO_2, and what mass of HCl would be required?

A blast furnace could produce about 700 tonnes of iron a day. How much iron (III) oxide would be consumed? Assuming coke is pure carbon, how much coke would be needed to produce the necessary carbon monoxide?

$$Fe_2O_3(s) + 3CO(g) \rightarrow 2Fe(l) + 3CO_2(g)$$

$$2C(s) + O_2(g) \rightarrow 2CO(g)$$

QUANTITATIVE CHEMISTRY

(The suitability of indicators is covered in Topic 8 of Module 2). This may be done to find the purity of a substance, say, or to produce a **standard solution** for use in another titration.

A standard solution is one which can be made of known concentration by weighing out the solute concerned. The solute must

1 be available commercially in a high state of purity
2 be stable over long periods of time
3 not decompose when dissolved in water
4 not be volatile, so losses due to evaporation during weighing do not occur
5 not absorb water or carbon dioxide from the atmosphere.

A good primary standard alkali is anhydrous sodium carbonate; an acidic one is the solid strong acid, sulphamic acid, H_2NSO_3H.

Example 1
A solution of sodium carbonate contains 12.5 g of the anhydrous salt in $1\,dm^3$ of solution. When $25.0\,cm^3$ of this solution was titrated with a solution of hydrochloric acid $23.45\,cm^3$ of the acid was required. What was the concentration of the acid?

You should first write the equation for the reaction:

$$Na_2CO_3(s) + 2HCl(aq) \rightarrow 2NaCl(aq) + H_2O(l) + CO_2(g)$$

Firstly the concentration of the sodium carbonate solution must be found. Anhydrous sodium carbonate has a molar mass of $106\,g\,mol^{-1}$. The concentration of the solution is therefore

$$\frac{12.5\,g\,dm^{-3}}{106\,g\,mol^{-1}} = 0.118\,mol\,dm^{-3}$$

The amount of sodium carbonate used is, therefore

volume × concentration
$= 0.025\,dm^3 \times 0.118\,mol\,dm^{-3} = 0.00295\,mol.$

From the equation, 1 mol of Na_2CO_3 requires 2 mol HCl, so

mol HCl used $= 0.00295 \times 2 = 0.00590.$

This was contained in $23.5\,cm^3$ of solution, so the concentration of HCl is therefore

$$\frac{\text{moles of solute}}{\text{volume}} = \frac{0.00590\,mol}{0.0235\,dm^3}$$

$$= 0.251\,mol\,dm^{-3}$$

One of the greatest difficulties faced by examiners is in understanding calculations when candidates fail to also write in words what is being done; a load of numbers is dumped on the page, with no connections or explanation. It

A sample of pure anhydrous sodium carbonate weighing 1.00g was dissolved in water and the volume made to 200 cm³. Portions of 25.0cm³ of this solution were titrated with hydrochloric acid solution of concentration of 0.120 mol dm⁻³. What volume was required?

A sample of sodium carbonate crystals, Na₂CO₃.xH₂O, weighing 4.00g was dissolved in water and made to 250cm³. Portions of 25.0cm³ of this solution required 22.40cm³ of hydrochloric acid of concentration 0.125 mol dm⁻³ for neutralisation. Find x.

is worth remembering that a lot of credit can be often be given for calculations which have the wrong answer, if the examiner can see from what has been written that many of the principles used in the work are correct.

Example 2
Solutions have frequently been diluted to obtain the solution which is titrated, but the question concerns the original solution.

A solution of sulphuric acid was made by pipetting $1.00\,cm^3$ of concentrated sulphuric acid into a $500\,cm^3$ graduated flask, and making to the mark with pure water. The solution was well mixed, and $25.0\,cm^3$ portions titrated with sodium hydroxide solution of concentration $0.1.00\,mol\,dm^{-3}$, using phenolphthalein indicator. An average volume of $19.8\,cm^3$ of sodium hydroxide was needed. Find the concentration of the original acid.

$$H_2SO_4(aq) + 2NaOH(aq) \rightarrow Na_2SO_4(aq) + 2H_2O(l)$$
$$mol\ NaOH = 0.0198 \times 0.1 = 1.98 \times 10^{-3}$$

Since 1 mol sulphuric acid requires 2 mol NaOH,

$$mol\ H_2SO_4 = \frac{1.98 \times 10^{-3}}{2} = 9.9 \times 10^{-4}$$

This is the amount of acid in $25.0\,cm^3$ of diluted solution; the concentration of acid is therefore

$$9.9 \times 10^{-4} \times \frac{500}{25} \times \frac{1000}{1} = 19.8\,mol\,dm^{-3}$$

The factor of 500/25 arises because $25\,cm^3$ was taken from $500\,cm^3$, and the 1000/1 factor because that diluted solution was made from $1\,cm^3$ of the concentrated acid, whereas the answer is required for $1000\,cm^3$ of the concentrated acid.

Example 3
Some titration problems concern substances which are insoluble, for which a slightly different strategy is required. This example demonstrates back-titration, used here to find the purity of a sample of chalk. Since chalk is insoluble in water, it is reacted with a known excess of acid, the acid remaining then being titrated with standard alkali.

A sample of $1.500\,g$ of chalk was reacted with $50.0\,cm^3$ of hydrochloric acid of concentration $1.00\,mol\,dm^{-3}$, which is an excess. When reaction had ceased, the solution was transferred quantitatively to a $250\,cm^3$ graduated flask, and made to the mark with pure water. Portions of $25.0\,cm^3$ of the well mixed solution were titrated with sodium hydroxide solution of concentration $0.1\,mol\,dm^{-3}$, using screened methyl orange indicator; on average a volume of $24.5\,cm^3$ was required. What is the percentage purity of the chalk?

$$CaCO_3(s) + 2HCl(aq) \rightarrow CaCl_2(aq) + H_2O(l) + CO_2(g)$$

$$HCl(aq) + NaOH(aq) \rightarrow NaCl(aq) + H_2O(l)$$

Molar mass of $CaCO_3 = 40 + 12 + (3 \times 16) = 100 \, \text{g mol}^{-1}$

The titration determines the amount of hydrochloric acid remaining after the chalk has reacted.

$$\text{Mol of NaOH} = \text{mol of HCl unreacted}$$
$$= 0.0245 \times 0.100 = 2.45 \times 10^{-3} \text{ in } 25.0 \text{ cm}^3$$

Thus total amount of HCl unreacted $= 2.45 \times 10^{-3} \times \dfrac{250}{25}$
$$= 0.0245 \, \text{mol}$$

Original amount of HCl taken $= 0.050 \times 1.00 = 0.050 \, \text{mol}$

Thus amount of HCl used to react with the $CaCO_3 = 0.050 - 0.0245$
$$= 0.0255 \, \text{mol}$$

Therefore the amount of $CaCO_3 = \dfrac{0.0255}{2} = 0.0128 \, \text{mol}$

Thus the mass of $CaCO_3 = 0.0128 \, \text{mol} \times 100 \, \text{g mol}^{-1} = 1.280 \, \text{g}$

% purity of the $CaCO_3 = \dfrac{1.280 \times 100}{1.500} = 85.3\%$

Example 4

Sometimes a substance undergoes reaction to form another substance which is then titrated. Methanal, HCHO, reacts with ammonium salts to give acid, which can then be titrated directly with base. This is a much simpler method than back-titration (Example 6) but should not be used with ammonium chloride since the hydrochloric acid produced reacts with methanal to give an extremely toxic compound.

Ammonium nitrate weighing 3.205 g was dissolved in water in a graduated flask, and the volume made to 250 cm³ with pure water. Portions of 25.0 cm³ of the solution were treated with 5 cm³ of 40% aqueous methanal solution, and allowed to stand for a few minutes. The mixture was then titrated with 0.1 mol dm⁻³ sodium hydroxide solution using phenolphthalein indicator; on average a volume of 37.5 cm³ was required . Find the percentage purity of the ammonium nitrate.

The reaction between methanal and the ammonium salt is

$$4NH_4NO_3(aq) + 6HCHO(aq) \rightarrow 4HNO_3(aq) + (CH_2)_6N_4(aq)$$

Thus one mole of ammonium salt gives one mole of acid. The other substance, hexamethylenetetramine, is neutral. The titration reaction is

$$HNO_3(aq) + NaOH(aq) \rightarrow NaNO_3(aq) + H_2O(l)$$

Molar mass of $NH_4NO_3 = 14 + 4 + 14 + (3 \times 16) = 80 \, \text{g mol}^{-1}$

$$\text{Mol NaOH} = 0.0375 \times 0.1 = 3.75 \times 10^{-3} = \text{mol HNO}_3$$
$$= \text{mol NH}_4\text{NO}_3 \text{ in } 25 \text{ cm}^3 \text{ of solution}$$

A solution of hydrochloric acid of volume 25.0 cm³ was pipetted onto a piece of marble which is calcium carbonate. When all action had ceased, 1.30g of the marble had dissolved. Find the concentration of the acid.

Thus the total amount of ammonium nitrate is

$$3.75 \times 10^{-3} \times \frac{250}{25} = 0.0375 \, \text{mol}$$

and the mass is $0.0375 \, \text{mol} \times 80 \, \text{g mol}^{-1} = 3.00 \, \text{g}$

Therefore, % purity of the salt $= \dfrac{3.00 \times 100}{3.205} = 93.6\%.$

Example 5

Ammonium salts can also be determined by back-titration. The salt is heated with excess sodium hydroxide solution, which liberates ammonia (it is the qualitative test for ammonium ions):

$$NH_4^+(aq) + OH^-(aq) \rightarrow NH_3(g) + H_2O(l)$$

The ammonia is absorbed in a known amount, which must be an excess, of acid, and the unreacted acid is titrated with sodium hydroxide solution.

Ammonium sulphate weighing 1.70 g was heated with excess sodium hydroxide solution, and the ammonia liberated was absorbed in 50.0 cm^3 of hydrochloric acid of concentration 1.00 mol dm^{-3}. This solution was transferred quantitatively to a graduated flask, and made to exactly 250 cm^3 with pure water. Portions of 25.0 cm^3 of this solution were titrated with sodium hydroxide solution of concentration 0.100 mol dm^{-3}, using methyl orange indicator. An average of 26.4 cm^3 was required. Find the percentage purity of the ammonium sulphate.

$$NH_3(aq) + HCl(aq) \rightarrow NH_4Cl(aq)$$

$$HCl(aq) + NaOH(aq) \rightarrow NaCl(aq) + H_2O(l)$$

Mol of NaOH $= 0.0264 \times 0.1 = 2.64 \times 10^{-3}$
$= $ mol of HCl remaining in 25 cm^3

Thus total amount of HCl remaining $= 2.64 \times 10^{-3} \times \dfrac{250}{25} = 0.0264 \, \text{mol}$

Original amount of HCl $= 0.05 \times 1.00 = 0.05 \, \text{mol}$

Amount of HCl used $= $ mol of NH$_3$ absorbed $= 0.050 - 0.0264$
$= 0.0236 \, \text{mol}$

1 mol ammonium sulphate gives 2 mol NH$_3$,

Therefore mol of ammonium sulphate originally present
$= \dfrac{0.0236}{2} = 0.0118 \, \text{mol}$

Mass of ammonium sulphate $= 0.0118 \, \text{mol} \times 132 \, \text{g mol}^{-1} = 1.56 \, \text{g}$

% purity of ammonium sulphate $= \dfrac{1.56}{1.70} \times 100 = 91.8\%$

A sample of impure ammonium sulphate weighing 1.852 g was dissolved in water and made to 250 cm³. Portions of 25.0 cm³ of this solution were treated with excess sodium hydroxide and boiled. This liberated ammonia which was absorbed in 50.0 cm³ of 0.106 mol dm⁻³ hydrochloric acid (an excess). When distillation was complete, the acid remaining required 25.5 cm³ of 0.102 mol dm⁻³ sodium hydroxide for neutralisation. Find the percentage purity of the ammonium nitrate.

A solution of 50.0 cm³ of hydrogen peroxide was diluted to 1 dm³. Portions of 25.0 cm³ of this solution were acidified with dilute sulphuric acid, and titrated with 0.02 mol dm⁻³ KMnO₄ solution; 23.9 cm³ was required. Find the concentration of the original hydrogen peroxide.

$$2MnO_4^- + 5H_2O_2 + 6H^+ \rightarrow 2Mn^{2+} + 5O_2 + 8H_2O$$

Example 6

The variety of volumetric calculations is very large. The problem in Example 5 could, for instance, have asked for the percentage nitrogen in the ammonium sulphate sample. Since the amount of ammonia is known, the mass of nitrogen atoms present can easily be found.

$$\text{mol of } NH_3 = 0.0236 = \text{mol of N}$$

$$\text{mass of N} = 0.0236 \text{ mol} \times 14 \text{ g mol}^{-1} = 0.330 \text{ g}$$

$$\text{\% N in the ammonium sulphate} = \frac{0.330 \times 100}{1.700} = 19.4\%$$

Other titrations

Although explained in detail in Module 3, redox titrations do not differ in principle from acid/base titrations.

Example 7

Potassium manganate(VII) reacts with iron(II) ions according to the equation:

$$MnO_4^-(aq) + 5Fe^{2+}(aq) + 8H^+(aq) \rightarrow Mn^{2+}(aq) + 5Fe^{3+}(aq) + 4H_2O(l)$$

Solutions of iron(II) are titrated with potassium manganate(VII) which, being intensely purple, is its own indicator.

Impure iron weighing 1.650 g was dissolved in 100 cm³ of dilute sulphuric acid in a graduated flask, and the solution was made to 250 cm³ with pure water. Portions of 25.0 cm³ of this iron(II) solution were titrated with potassium manganate(VII) solution of concentration 0.02 mol dm⁻³, 28.5 cm³ being required on average. Find the percentage purity of the iron.

$$Fe(s) + H_2SO_4(aq) \rightarrow FeSO_4(aq) + H_2(g)$$

$$\text{Moles of } MnO^{4-} = 0.0285 \times 0.020 = 5.70 \times 10^{-4}$$

$$\text{Moles of } Fe^{2+} \text{ in 25 cm}^3 \text{ of solution} = 5 \times 5.70 \times 10^{-4} = 2.85 \times 10^{-3}$$

$$\text{Thus the total moles of } Fe^{2+} = 2.85 \times 10^{-3} \times \frac{250}{25} = 0.0285$$

$$\text{Mass of Fe} = 0.0285 \text{ mol} \times 56 \text{ g mol}^{-1} = 1.596 \text{ g}$$

$$\text{\% Fe in the sample} = \frac{1.596}{1.650} \times 100 = 96.7\%$$

Problems involving gas volumes

As already mentioned the Italian chemist Avogadro proposed that equal volumes of all gases at the same temperature and pressure contain the same number of particles. The molar volume of a gas is the most useful quantity, that is that volume, at a specified temperature and pressure, which contains

6.02×10^{23} particles of the gas. The precise definition uses $0\,^\circ C$ and $1\,atm$ pressure, where the volume is $22.414\,dm^3$, but no principle is lost if the value is taken as $24\,dm^3$ at room temperature and pressure (Figure 2.2). The appalling vagueness of this statement within a quantitative science will not be lost on you, so the statement that the molar volume of any gas at the temperature and pressure of the experiment is $24\,dm^3$, is preferable. You don't need to know what the temperature and pressure actually are. This statement is included implicitly in the examples which follow.

The result of the Avogadro statement is that gases react in volumes which are proportional to the mole ratios in the equation.

Example 8
Propane burns in oxygen to give carbon dioxide and water. What volume of oxygen is needed to burn $10\,cm^3$ of propane, and what volume of CO_2 results?

The volumes are in the proportions stated in the equation:

$$C_3H_8(g) \; + \; 5O_2(g) \; = \; 3CO_2(g) \; + \; 4H_2O(l)$$

$\quad 10\,cm^3 \qquad 50\,cm^3 \qquad 30\,cm^3$

Example 9
A weighed piece of marble is reacted with hydrochloric acid, and is dried and reweighed when all action has ceased. The mass loss was $2.33\,g$; what volume of carbon dioxide was evolved?

$$CaCO_3(s) \; + \; 2HCl(aq) \rightarrow CaCl_2(aq) \; + \; CO_2(g) \; + \; H_2O(l)$$

$$\text{Moles } CaCO_3 \; = \; \frac{2.33\,g}{100\,g\,mol^{-1}} = 0.0233$$

$$\text{Thus moles of } CO_2 \text{ produced} = 0.0233$$

Therefore volume of $CO_2 = 0.0233\,mol \times 24\,dm^3\,mol^{-1} = 0.56\,dm^3$.

Dry hydrogen chloride gas of volume $120\,cm^3$ was absorbed in water and the solution made to a volume of $100\,cm^3$. What is the concentration of this solution, and what volume of $0.125\,mol\,dm^{-3}$ sodium hydroxide solution would be required to exactly neutralise it? (Molar volume of gas at the temperature and pressure of the experiment is $24\,dm^3$).

What mass of phosphorus is required to make $200\,cm^3$ of phosphine, PH_3, via the reaction:
$P_4(s) + 3NaOH\,(aq) + 3H_2O(l) \rightarrow 3NaH_2PO_4(aq) + PH_3(g)$

$10.0\,cm^3$ of a hydrocarbon C_4H_x reacts with an excess of oxygen at $150^\circ C$ and $1atm$ pressure. The products occupy a volume $10\,cm^3$ greater than the reactants at this temperature and pressure. Find x.

3 Bonding and structure

Bonds

Atoms would not be of much interest if they weren't able to join together; there would be no chemistry, after all. Their joining is not random, though, and any model of bonding must be able to explain why many things cannot easily be pulled apart, yet people do not permanently bond to the chair on which they are sitting.

A fundamental feature of chemistry is that the bulk properties of substances, whether they are hard or soft, soluble or not, conductors or non-conductors of electricity, are explicable in terms of the bonding between atoms and molecules. The properties depend on the nature of the bonds, and on exactly how the bonds are distributed throughout the material. Bonding occurs where atoms or molecules can rearrange their electrons to give lower energy arrangements of electrons and nuclei than were present before bonding took place.

Until now you have probably divided bonds into two types, the ionic bond where positively and negatively charged ions are held together by the attraction of their opposite charges, or the covalent bond where electrons are shared between the bonded atoms. Most compounds have some of the characteristics of both, though tending in major properties towards one or the other. Thus sodium chloride is almost completely ionic (Figure 3.1), but lithium iodide shows some covalent characteristics; chlorine or hydrogen molecules are completely covalent, but hydrogen fluoride has electrons which are very unequally shared and the bond shows some polarity or separation of charge. Some compounds have both sorts of bond; NH_4NO_3 has ammonium and nitrate ions held electrostatically, but the atoms in the ions themselves are covalently bonded.

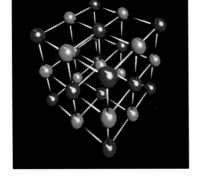

Figure 3.1 The naCl lattice

The present approach to bonding will ask firstly how the predominant type may be predicted, and secondly how far the compound is likely to deviate from that type. The notion that metal bonds to non-metal with ionic bonds and non-metal with non-metal by covalent bonds was useful at GCSE, but must now be improved to a more informed approach.

The ionic bond

Ions

Ionic bonds are formed between particles which have a net electrical charge. Positive ions are called **cations**, since they are attracted to the negative cathode during electrolysis; negative ions are called **anions**, and migrate to the anode on electrolysis. Either sort of ion can contain one or more atoms:

Simple cations are metal atoms which have lost one or more electrons, e.g. K^+, Ca^{2+}. They have more protons than electrons, hence the positive charge.

Complex cations are usually, but not invariably, formed from d-block metals (Topic 4), and contain a metal ion joined to a number of **ligands**, which are molecules or ions bonded to the metal ion by dative covalent bonds (see next sub-section and Topic 4). Examples are $[Cu(H_2O)^6]^{2+}$, $[Mn(H_2O)_6]^{2+}$.

Polyatomic cations have several atoms bonded covalently, the whole structure having a positive charge, e.g. NH_4^+

Anions have more electrons than protons. Simple anions are those of non-metals, e.g. Cl^-, O^{2-}. Complex anions exist where the groups around the central metal ion are themselves negative, e.g. the iron(II) complex $[Fe(CN)_6]^{4-}$. Polyatomic anions are common, derived from acids by the loss of one or more hydrogen ions, and include SO_4^{2-}, NO_3^-, CH_3COO^-, MnO_4^- and $Cr_2O_7^{2-}$.

Features favouring ionic bonding

Ionic bonds (Figure 3.2) are favoured if
- the metal has a low ionisation energy
- the non-metal has a high electron affinity (electron gain energy)
- the metal forms large ions of low charge
- the nonmetal forms small ions of high charge.

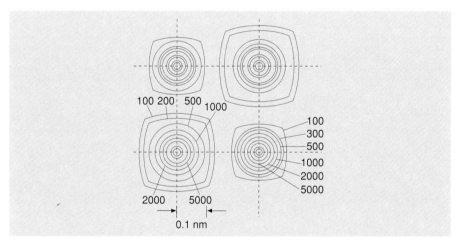

Figure 3.2 Electron density map for sodium chloride

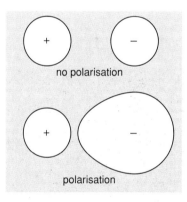

Figure 3.3 The ionic model has no polarisation; deviations arise because polarisation gives some covalent character

The extent to which the bonds formed are ionic depends on the effect which the cation, generally the smaller ion, has on the anion. Small cations of high charge have a high charge density, and this may be able to distort the electron cloud around the anion so that there is some degree of electron sharing between the cation and anion. This is polarisation; small highly charged cations are very polarising, large anions are polarisable (Figure 3.3).

The ionic model for crystals enables the **lattice enthalpy** to be calculated. The calculated value assumes no polarisation, so a comparison between this and the experimental value will give an estimate of the extent of covalence within the crystal. The presence of covalence increases the lattice enthalpy.

Consider the effect of changing the size of the cation whilst keeping the anion the same. As the cation gets larger, its charge density decreases and it becomes

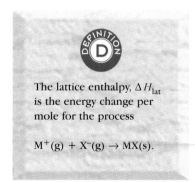

The lattice enthalpy, ΔH_{lat} is the energy change per mole for the process

$$M^+(g) + X^-(g) \rightarrow MX(s).$$

less polarising. Therefore the extent of covalence will fall and the difference between calculated and experimental ΔH_{lat}, will fall. Table 3.1 shows this effect for the chlorides of group 2.

Table 3.1 *The lattice enthalpies of group 2 chlorides*

Chloride	Cation radius/pm	ΔH_{lat}/kJ mol^{-1}		
		Experimental	Calculated	Difference
MgCl$_2$	72	2526	2326	200
CaCl$_2$	100	2258	2223	35
SrCl$_2$	113	2156	2127	29
BaCl$_2$	136	2056	2033	23

Criticise, by considering the energy changes involved, the statement that 'when sodium and chlorine react they do so because the ions that result have octets of electrons.'

Consider now the effect of changing the size of the anion. As the anions increase in size, they become more polarisable since the outer electrons are further from the nucleus, less tightly held, and more prone to distortion. Similar data to that shown in Table 3.1 is given in Table 3.2, for the halides of magnesium. The more polarisable iodide ion leads to greater covalence in MgI$_2$ compared with MgF$_2$.

Table 3.2 *The lattice enthalpies of magnesium halides*

Magnesium halide	Radius/pm	ΔH_{lat}/kJ mol^{-1}		
		Experimental	Calculated	Difference
MgF$_2$	133	2957	2913	44
MgCl$_2$	180	2526	2326	200
MgBr$_2$	195	2440	2097	343
MgI$_2$	215	2329	1944	385

Lastly, consider the effect of cationic charge. The greater the charge, the more polarising the cation. The difference between the experimental and calculated values of ΔH_{lat} for NaCl is 10 kJ mol^{-1}; for magnesium chloride it is 200 kJ mol^{-1}. Aluminium chloride is a covalent solid, and silicon tetrachloride is a covalent liquid at room temperature.

The covalent bond

The sharing of electrons

Covalent bonds are formed by sharing electron pairs, one pair to a bond. For most covalent substances, this is so that hydrogen obtains 2 electrons in its outer shell and other atoms obtain 8 (the so-called 'octet rule'), though atoms beyond the second period (Li to Ne) can 'expand the octet' and form more than the four bonds which 8 electrons allow. SF$_6$, where sulphur has 12 outer shell electrons, is one such compound. Only those elements which have d-orbitals available for bonding can form more than four bonds.

State with reasons, which of each of the following pairs of compounds would show a greater degree of covalent character:
(a) LiCl and CsCl; (b) MgCl$_2$ and BaCl$_2$; (c) NaCl and AlCl$_3$; (d) ClF$_3$ and IF$_3$.

The **dative covalent bond** is formed where both electrons in the bond come from the same atom. Examples include the ammonium ion, NH$_4^+$, and the hydroxonium ion H_3O^+, where the bonds, once formed, are no different from the other bonds in the ion, and in transition metal complexes (Topic 4) between the ligand and the central metal ion.

Orbitals and covalent bonds

A covalent bond is formed by overlap of atomic orbitals so that the electron density rises between the bonded atoms. A non-dative bond is formed by two one-electron orbitals overlapping to give a two electron bonding orbital; a dative bond arises from a two-electron orbital donating electron density into an 'empty' orbital on the accepting atom. Have a look at the orbital shapes again (Topic 1) before continuing.

When the orbitals overlap they give molecular orbitals where the electron density extends over at least two atoms. Benzene has orbitals extending over six atoms, and graphite has orbitals over vast numbers in each sheet of atoms (see Bonding and properties, later in this chapter). Examples of molecules containing single bonds are shown in Figures 3.4 and 3.5. Several of these contain two sorts of electron pair; **bond pairs**, and non-bonding or **lone pairs** which are not involved in bonds but which could become so in some cases. The total number of electron pairs is important in determining the shape of a molecule. (This is discussed further in the final section of this chapter.)

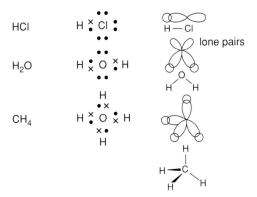

Figure 3.4 Single bonds, represented by dot and cross diagrams and by overlapping orbitals

Figure 3.5 Model of a water molecule

All of these molecules have electron density which surrounds the line joining the two atoms. Such bonds, arising from head-on overlap between orbitals, are called sigma bonds, symbolised σ-bonds. Other bonds arise from sideways overlap of orbitals, for example two p orbitals as shown in Figure 3.6.

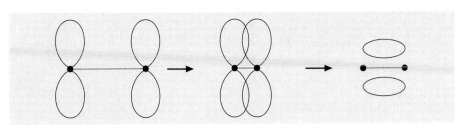

Figure 3.6 Sideways overlap of p orbitals, forming a pi bond

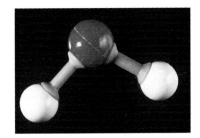

Figure 3.7 Linus Pauling, exponent of the nature of the chemical bond.

These bonds arise where atoms form multiple, that is **double** or **triple bonds**, and they are called pi bonds, also written as π-bonds. Double bonds contain one σ-bond and one π-bond; triple bonds contain one σ-bond and two π-bonds. So although multiple bonds are written as though they are equivalent in molecular structure, they are not.

Polarity in bonds and in molecules

A covalent bond is polar if the electrons in the bond are unequally shared. This depends on the difference in electronegativity of the bonded atoms, the larger the electronegativity difference the more polar the bond.

The electronegativity is a measure of how strongly an atom attracts electrons when in a covalent bond. It is not the same as electron gain energy, which is precisely defined for an individual atom in the gas phase (see section on Electron affinity in Topic 1). The smaller an atom is, the closer the bonding electrons can come to the nucleus, and so the more attraction there will be; small atoms therefore have high electronegativity. Electronegativity increases from left to right across the Periodic Table, and falls going down a group. There are various scales of electronegativity, the most commonly used being the Pauling (see Figure 3.7) scale in which the most electronegative element, fluorine, is arbitrarily assigned a value of 4. Pauling electronegativities are given in Figure 3.8.

H 2.1	He																
Li 1.0	Be 1.5											B 2.0	C 2.5	N 3.0	O 3.5	F 4.0	Ne
Na 0.9	Mg 1.2											Al 1.5	Si 1.8	P 2.1	S 2.5	Cl 3.0	Ar
K 0.8	Ca 1.0	Sc 1.3	Ti 1.5	V 1.6	Cr 1.6	Mn 1.5	Fe 1.8	Co 1.8	Ni 1.8	Cu 1.9	Zn 1.6	Ga 1.6	Ge 1.8	As 2.0	Se 2.4	Br 2.8	Kr
Rb 0.8	Sr 1.0	Y 1.2	Zr 1.4	Nb 1.6	Mo 1.8	Tc 1.9	Ru 2.2	Rh 2.2	Pd 2.2	Ag 1.9	Cd 1.7	In 1.7	Sn 1.8	Sb 1.9	Te 2.1	I 2.5	Xe
Cs 0.7	Ba 0.9	La 1.1	Hf 1.3	Ta 1.5	W 1.7	Re 1.9	Os 2.2	Ir 2.2	Pt 2.2	Au 2.4	Hg 1.9	Tl 1.8	Pb 1.8	Bi 1.9	Po 2.0	At 2.2	Rn
Fr	Ra	Sc															

Ce 1.1	Pr 1.1	Nd 1.2	Pm 1.2	Sm 1.2	Eu 1.1	Gd 1.1	Tb 1.2	Dy 1.1	Ho 1.2	Er 1.2	Tm 1.2	Yb 1.1	Lu 1.2
Th 1.3	Pa 1.5	U 1.7	Np 1.3	Pu 1.3	Am 1.3	Cm 1.3	Bk 1.3	Cf 1.3	Es 1.3	Fm 1.3	Md 1.3	No 1.3	Lr

Figure 3.8 Pauling electronegativities of the elements.

Electronegativity differences affect not only the polarity of the bond, but also the bond length, with larger differences giving shorter bonds than would be expected from the radii of the atoms alone.

Although a molecule may have polar bonds it does not follow that the molecule itself is polar. The dipole which the polar bond forms experiences a turning effect or torque in an electric field, and the polarity's direction is therefore important. The positive and negative ends of the dipoles are usually represented by the symbols δ^+ and δ^-. The molecule will be polar if the dipoles on each of the bonds do not cancel, so that water and ammonia are polar molecules. However CO_2, which is linear, and CCl_4, which is tetrahedral, are not polar since the dipoles from each of the bonds cancel in the molecule as a whole (Figure 3.9).

For each of the following state with reasons whether or not it has a dipole; if it has, show its direction.
(a) $CHCl_3$; (b) PH_3; (c) BCl_3; (d) $BeCl_2$; (e) CS_2; (f) NCl_3; (g) CH_3OH; (h) cis-ClCH=CHCl; (i) trans-ClCH=CHCl.

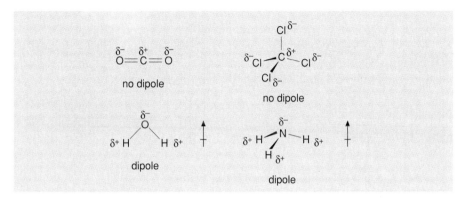

Figure 3.9 Molecules with polar bonds do not necessarily have an overall dipole moment. (The arrows show the direction of the dipole with the cross at the positive end.)

Intermolecular forces

Bonds within molecules (intramolecular bonds) are strong and difficult to break, which is why many reactions involving covalent substances are slow. Bonds between molecules, or intermolecular bonds, are relatively weak, and rely on dipole–dipole attractions which may be between permanent dipoles (the strongest) or between temporary or induced dipoles, which are weaker. Temporary or induced dipole forces are generically called **van der Waals' forces**.

Hydrogen bonding

The strongest intermolecular force is the hydrogen bond. It is an electrostatic attraction between a strongly δ^+ hydrogen atom attached covalently to a fluorine, nitrogen or oxygen atom, and a strongly δ^- fluorine, nitrogen or oxygen atom on another molecule In some cases the interaction may be within the same molecule. The strongest hydrogen bond is in hydrogen flouride, HF, $150\,kJ\,mol^{-1}$, but many are in the range $60–20\,kJ\,mol^{-1}$. H-bonds are usually shown as broken lines, and are longer than covalent bonds (Figure 3.10).

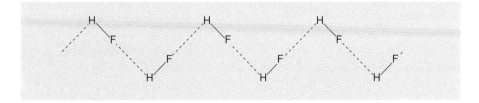

Figure 3.10 Hydrogen bonding between hydrogen fluoride molecules

BONDING AND STRUCTURE

Hydrogen bonding has a considerable effect on the properties of the substances which have it. Water has extensive H-bonds in the liquid, with the result that water has a much higher boiling temperature, T_b, than would be expected by comparison with the other hydrides of group 6. The same is true of ammonia, NH_3 compared with other Group 5 hydrides, and of hydrogen fluoride compared with other hydrides in group 7. The effects are illustrated in Figure 3.11.

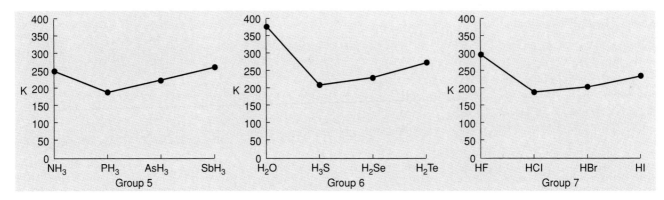

Figure 3.11 *Boiling temperatures of groups 5, 6 and 7 hydrides*

As water cools, the liquid contracts, and hydrogen bonds form in greater quantity. Since they are long, they space the molecules out, so the density of the liquid falls. At 0°C the liquid freezes to a structure where the molecules are held in rings of six, each molecule being H-bonded to two others. This very ordered and open structure has a lower density than liquid water at 0°C, so ice shows the unique property of floating in its liquid – and enables iced drinks to cool by convection and save the bother of stirring them.

H-bonds affect solubility in water. Compounds which can H-bond with the water will be very soluble even if they have quite a lot of organic content. Sugars, which have large numbers of OH groups which H-bond with water, are amongst the most soluble organic substances known. Benzene, C_6H_6, does not dissolve significantly in water but phenol, C_6H_5OH, is appreciably soluble; smaller alcohols are miscible with water in all proportions.

The structure of proteins and of nucleic acids depends strongly on H-bonding. Proteins are polymers of amino acids, and long sections of the molecule coil into helices as H-bonds hold the turns of the helix together. The same is true of cellulose, a polymer of glucose. Nucleic acids, with their famous double helix structure, have the two halves of the helix attached by hydrogen bonding.

Dipole–dipole forces

Weaker forces exist between molecules which are permanently polar but which cannot form H-bonds. The δ^+ and δ^- parts of the molecules attract electrostatically, and give boiling temperatures which are significantly higher than those of non-polar molecules of similar molar mass. Thus propanone, CH_3COCH_3, and butane, $CH_3CH_2CH_2CH_3$, have the same molar mass ($58\,\text{g mol}^{-1}$) but the polar propanone boils at 329 K, while butane boils at 273 K.

Dispersion forces

Temporary dipoles form between molecules because the electron density is somewhat mobile within the molecule, and cause temporary δ^+ and δ^- areas within the molecule. A δ^+ on one molecule will induce a δ^- on a nearby one, which then causes further δ^+ to form, and so on (Figure 3.12).

These dipole effects are constantly shifting, but there is a net attraction between the molecules. The larger the molecule, the more opportunities there are for these dipoles to form, and the greater the intermolecular force and hence the boiling or melting temperature. The increase of T_b with increasing chain length for the alkanes, for example, is due to the increasing size of the molecules and the increased dispersion forces between the molecules.

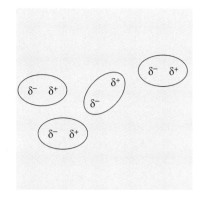

Figure 3.12 Temporary dipoles lead to a net attraction between molecules

Bonding and properties

The bulk properties of substances depend on the bonding. We shall consider each type in turn.

Giant molecular substances

These have covalent bonds which extend over long distances in the solid; a crystal of visible size can consist essentially of one molecule. The best-known example is diamond, which has layers of chair shaped six-membered rings of carbon joined in every direction by σ-bonds (Figure 3.13). Silicon dioxide has a related structure. Giant structures have extremely high melting temperatures, for example over 3800 K for diamond, and because bonds throughout the crystal are strong the crystals are very hard. The crystal lattice is very stiff and readily transmits vibration, so diamond is a good thermal conductor, but there are no free electrons and no ions, so it is a very poor electrical conductor.

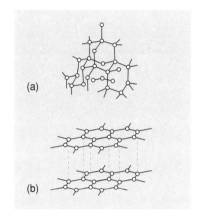

Figure 3.13 Molecular structure of (a) diamond and (b) graphite

Graphite is unique (Figure 3.14). The four bonds between the carbon atoms are 3 σ-, and one π-bonds forming sheets of flat hexagons (Figure 3.13). The π-electrons are not localised between the carbon atoms, instead they are free to move along but not between the layers. Van der Waals' forces attract the layers to one another, but these are much weaker than the bonds within the layers. The crystal therefore consists of layers of giant molecules, and has a high melting temperature (over 3900 K), but the layers can slide over one another so the substance feels greasy and is used as a dry lubricant. The free electrons allow conduction of electricity along the layers only, not at right angles to them, unlike in metals where the electrons can travel in any direction.

Ionic substances

These also have strong bonds throughout their lattice, these bonds being electrostatic. Thus they have high melting temperatures, which are however related to the extent of ionicity of the bonding.

They are hard but, if stressed, layers of the crystal may slide so that ions of the same charge come next to one another and repel, thus breaking the crystal. In other words, they are brittle.

Figure 3.14 (a) Diamond; (b) hexagonal crystal structure of graphite

The solid does not conduct electricity, since there are no charge carriers which can move, but molten ionic substances have mobile ions which will allow

Silicon shows a similar structure to diamond. It has a lower melting temperature, 1683K compared with about 3800K for diamond. Suggest reasons for this. Silicon and carbon are both in group 4.

There is no silicon structure corresponding to graphite. Suggest why not.

Suggest why polymers do not usually have a sharp melting temperature, but melt over a range of temperatures.

conduction. Such conduction is always accompanied by chemical changes at the electrodes, and is of course electrolysis. Ionic compounds are often soluble in water; this is discussed in more detail later in this chapter.

Molecular covalent substances

Such compounds are bonded strongly within the molecule, but weakly between molecules. The properties depend on the size of the molecules and on the strength of the intermolecular bonds. So small, non-polar molecules give gases or volatile liquids (alkanes, alkenes); heavier members of these series (paraffin waxes) are soft, low-melting point solids. More polar substances will give volatile liquids even for the smallest molecules, e.g. ethanal CH_3CHO, propanone CH_3COCH_3. Substances with hydrogen bonds (water, alcohols) have much higher boiling temperatures than would be expected from their masses.

Since there are no free electrons, all being used in bonding, molecular covalent substances are non-conductors of electricity.

Polymers

These materials may be synthetic or natural, but all contain long chains which may be cross-linked by covalent bonds, or be held by H-bonds or dispersion forces, or, in the case of silicates, by Coulomb forces between the negatively-charged chains of silicate and metal ions. The mechanical properties of the polymer depend on the extent of cross linking, and on whether crystallites, which are areas of crystallinity where the polymer chains are aligned, can form.

Synthetic organic polymers

Synthetic organic polymers are made from alkenes by addition reactions, or from reactions between organic molecules having two functional groups which can undergo condensation reactions (Topic 14, Module 2, and Topic 23, Module 4). They are mixtures, since the chain length cannot be exactly determined, and so do not show a sharp melting temperature. Instead they soften over a range of temperature which depends on their structure. Polymers which are formed by radical reactions, for example low density poly(ethene), are branched and cross-linked because the intermediate radicals are so reactive and rather indiscriminate in their attack. There are few crystallites, and the material is flexible, elastic and translucent.

The ultimate polymer (for now) is a result of the highly controlled type of polymerisation invented by Ziegler and Natta using a catalyst complex of titanium trichloride and triethylaluminium. With this it is possible to determine that side chains are all on the same side of the chain, alternate to one side or another, or are aligned at random. Because the conditions are more controlled than in radical polymerisations, there are more crystallites, and the polymers are stiffer and are opaque.

Natural polymers

Natural organic polymers include proteins, polysaccharides such as cellulose, starch and glycogen, and nucleic acids. All of these are produced by condensation reactions. Proteins may have structural functions (muscle, say) or catalytic ones (enzymes).

Inorganic polymers are widely distributed, for example there are the hugely abundant silicates, and phosphoric acid also forms a variety of polymeric structures on heating. The details of natural polymer chemistry are outside our present concerns.

Intermolecular forces in the liquid state

The forces between molecules in liquids are no different in type from those of solids, merely in degree. So intermolecular forces in liquids can be van der Waals, dipole–dipole or hydrogen bonds. The difference is that the particles in liquids are more energetic than those in solids, so the bonds are not particularly directional and liquids have no particular shape. When a liquid boils, the particles have to be separated one from another, and they then have to be given enough energy to break free from the liquid surface, so the boiling temperatures of liquids depend on both the magnitude of the interparticular forces and the masses of the particles themselves.

In the noble gases, the interatomic forces are very small; the boiling temperatures rise with increasing relative atomic mass (Table 3.3). A similar point can be made with respect to the hydrides of Group 4. All the

Table 3.3 *The boiling temperatures of the noble gases*

Element	Relative atomic mass	T_b/K
helium	4.0	4
neon	20.2	27
argon	39.9	87
krypton	83.8	121
xenon	131.3	166

bonds in these molecules are polar, though the tetrahedral shape means that the molecule as a whole is not since the polarities cancel. The boiling temperatures increase with increasing size of the molecule (Table 3.4).

Table 3.4 *The boiling temperatures of Group 4 hydrides*

Hydride	Relative molecular mass	T_b/K
CH_4	16.0	81.6
SiH_4	32.1	161
GeH_4	76.6	185
SnH_4	122.7	221

(PbH_4 probably does not exist)

With the hydrides of Groups 5, 6 and 7, the pattern changes dramatically. The lightest elements in these groups are all electronegative enough to show hydrogen bonding as the principal intermolecular force in their hydrides. Hydrides of the heavier elements in these groups do not show the same ability, and so the boiling temperatures are much lower than those of the lightest ones. (see Figure 3.11).

Change of state

Solids have a fixed shape; the bonds between the particles in the lattice are strong enough to prevent the particles from moving large distances, though they will vibrate about a mean position in the crystal lattice. These vibrations arise because the crystal is not at absolute zero, and the amplitude of the vibrations increases with increasing temperature.

Consider what happens as a solid is heated. At some temperature the vibrations will be sufficient to overcome the forces holding the crystal together. This temperature, which is the melting temperature, T_m, will depend upon the strength of the interparticular forces. Thus a lot of hydrogen bonding produces materials of quite high melting temperature, for example glucose, whose $T_m = 423\,K$; whereas molecules of similar size with van der Waals forces only will have a much lower melting temperature, as with dodecane, whose $T_m = 264\,K$.

While the compound is melting, the temperature remains constant since the heat is being used to break the interparticular forces. Once the substance is liquid, further heating increases the energy of the particles, some of which will now have enough energy to break free from the liquid surface. This is how evaporation occurs. If the temperature continues to rise, the number of molecules escaping will also rise, and so will the vapour pressure of the liquid. At the boiling temperature T_b the vapour pressure of the liquid is the same as the external pressure, and bubbles of vapour are produced throughout the liquid, and it is boiling. The heat being put in to the liquid is being used to overcome the interparticular forces so that the molecules can escape the liquid, and so the temperature remains constant.

In the case of atomic or molecular substances, the vaporised particles are usually the same molecules or atoms that are present in the liquid. This is not always the case, though; the vapour of sodium contains Na_2, for example, and that from sulphur contains S_2 and S_4. In the case of ionic compounds, the vapours usually consist of ion pairs, sodium chloride vapour containing Na^+Cl^- pairs.

The hydration of ions in solution and the solubility of ionic compounds

A simple theory of solubility for ionic compounds, based solely on energy changes, cannot be stated. This is because the solubility of most substances is not controlled by enthalpy changes alone, any more than the direction of spontaneous change is so controlled in chemical reactions (Topic 6, Module 2). The problem cannot be examined generally without using the thermodynamic idea of entropy, and unfortunately quite small changes in entropy can have large consequences for solubility. This is beyond our present concerns, so we shall look only at compounds for which the enthalpy change, ΔH (the heat change at constant pressure during the process) is the governing factor.

When an ionic substance dissolves, the enthalpy change depends on

1 the lattice enthalpy, ΔH_{lat}, of the solid
2 the hydration enthalpy, ΔH_{hyd}, of the ions.

What type of intra- and intermolecular forces exist in each of the following materials? List the physical properties which each substance shows as a consequence of the bonding:

(a) solid xenon; (b) solid iodine; (c) diamond; (d) graphite; (e) ice; (f) liquid hydrogen fluoride; (g) glucose; (h) polyethene.

Sketch a graph of the temperature vs time as a substance is heated from just below its melting temperature to just above its boiling temperature.

Suggest reasons why sodium chloride vapour is regarded as a collection of ion pairs rather than as NaCl molecules.

The lattice enthalpy is defined as the enthalpy change per mole for the process

$$M^+(g) + X^-(g) \rightarrow MX(s),$$

that is the combination of the gaseous ions to form the solid crystal. Note that some books define the lattice enthalpy in the reverse (endothermic) direction, so be careful when you use other texts or data books. Some experimental lattice enthalpies are given in Table 3.5.

Table 3.5 *Some lattice enthalpies in kJ mol⁻¹*

Chlorides				Oxides	
LiCl	−846				
NaCl	−771	$MgCl_2$	−2493	MgO	−3889
KCl	−701	$CaCl_2$	−2237	CaO	−3513
RbCl	−675	$SrCl_2$	−2112	SrO	−3310
CsCl	−645	$BaCl_2$	−2018	BaO	−3152

The hydration enthalpy of a gaseous cation is defined as the heat change per mole for the process

$$M^+(g) + aq \rightarrow M^+(aq)$$

where 'aq' means enough water is used for there to be no further heat change on dilution of the solution. The equation for anions is similar. ΔH_{hyd} is exothermic. If it is roughly the same in magnitude as ΔH_{lat}, or is greater, then the heat needed to break the lattice is recouped by the hydration of the ions and the dissolution of the substance is energetically favoured, that is ΔH_{soln} is negative (ΔH_{soln} is the enthalpy change when a substance dissolves in a given solvent, to give a solution sufficiently dilute that addition of further solvent gives no further enthalpy change). Low solubility may be a result of high lattice enthalpy or low hydration enthalpy of the ions.

The enthalpy changes can be represented on the Hess's Law cycle (see Topic 6, Module 2) :

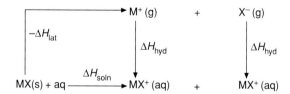

From Hess's Law:

$$\Delta H_{soln} = \Delta H_{hyd}(M^+) + \Delta H_{hyd}(X^-) - \Delta H_{lat}(MX)$$

The hydration of ions occurs because the polar water molecules are attracted to the charge on the ion (Figure 3.16). The extent of the hydration depends on the charge density on the ion, i.e. its charge per unit surface area, so the higher the charge and the smaller the ion, the higher the hydration enthalpy. Some hydration enthalpies are given in Table 3.6.

Figure 3.16 The hydration of ions

The same factors, charge and size, alter lattice enthalpies, so the solubility trend for a series of compounds depends on which factor changes the fastest.

The solubilities of hydroxides and sulphates are considered in Chapter 5, to which you should now refer.

Table 3.7 *Hydration enthalpies of some ions (in kJ mol^{-1})*

Group 1		Group 2		Group 3		Anions	
Li$^+$	−519					F$^-$	−506
Na$^+$	−406	Mg^{2+}	−1920	Al^{3+}	−4690	Cl$^-$	−364
K$^+$	−322	Ca^{2+}	−1650			Br$^-$	−335
Rb$^+$	−301	Sr^{2+}	−1480			I$^-$	−293
Cs$^+$	−276	Ba^{2+}	−1360				

To get a feel for hydration enthalpies, plot the hydration enthalpy against the ionic radius using the following data:

	Li$^+$	Na$^+$	K$^+$	Rb$^+$	CS$^+$
r/pm	60	95	133	148	169
ΔH_{hyd}/kJ mol^{-1}	−519	−406	−322	−293	−264

	F$^-$	Cl$^-$	Br$^-$	I$^-$	
r/pm	136	181	195	216	
ΔH_{hyd}/kJ mol^{-1}	−515	−381	−347	−305	

	Be^{2+}	Mg^{2+}	Ca^{2+}	Sr^{2+}	Ba^{2+}
r/pm	31	65	99	113	135
ΔH_{hyd}/kJ mol^{-1}	−2494	−1921	−1577	−1443	−1305

The shapes of molecules and ions

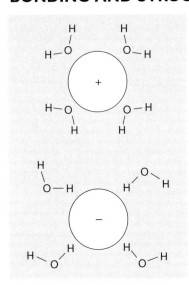

Figure 3.17 J.H. van't Hoff

The great German chemist Hermann Kolbe wrote in 1877 of the 'fantasies' of J.H. van't Hoff (Figure 3.17), who had postulated that molecules have definite shapes. Kolbe did not spare the feelings of his target in an amazingly vitriolic article which made reference to 'flights of fancy on a Pegasus from the veterinary college', van't Hoff being employed at the time at the veterinary college of Utrecht; but van't Hoff eventually was vindicated and received the first Nobel Prize in chemistry. Kolbe had by then been dead some sixteen years.

That molecules and polyatomic ions do have shapes is well known; we need to look at the rules which enable a prediction of them. There are two:

1 The shape adopted is the one that puts the electron pairs in the valence, i.e the outer shell, whether bonding or lone pairs, as far apart as possible.
2 The order of repulsion between the various sorts of electron pair is

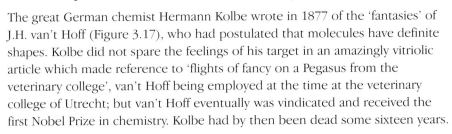

bp – bp *less than* **bp – lp** *less than* **lp – lp**.

where 'bp' means bonding or bond pair and 'lp' means lone pair.

Rule 2 does not affect the shape in a fundamental way, but does modify the bond angles somewhat. Consider some examples.

2 bond pairs

This arrangement is found in beryllium chloride vapour, $BeCl_2$, which is linear (the solid consists of polymeric chains), as shown in Figure 3.18(a). The bonds are as far apart as possible at 180°.

3 bond pairs

This produces a trigonal planar structure, where the molecule is flat and the bond angles are 120°. Boron trifluoride, BF_3, is a good example (Figure 3.18(b)).

4 bond pairs

The fundamental arrangement is tetrahedral, e.g. as in methane, and all other saturated carbon atoms, with a bond angle of 109.5° (Figure 3.18(c)).

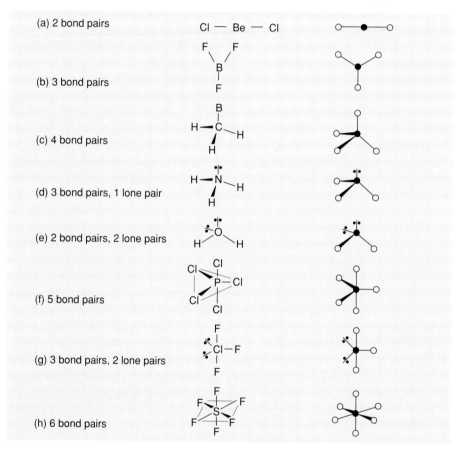

Figure 3.18 Molecular bonds and shapes

3 bond pairs, 1 lone pair

The arrangement of orbitals is tetrahedral, but since only three of the pairs are bonding pairs the molecule is called 'pyramidal', e.g. ammonia (Figure 3.18(d)). The repulsion between the lone pair and the bond pairs is more than that between the bond pairs because the lone pair is pulled towards the nucleus and is rather fatter than the other orbitals. The H–N–H bond angle is therefore compressed slightly to 107° from the tetrahedral angle of 109° 28'.

On forming the ammonium ion, the electrons all become bond pairs, and NH_4^+ is a regular tetrahedron. There is no difference between the dative bond and the other three once formed.

2 bond pairs, 2 lone pairs

This arrangement is found in water, whose molecule is bent as shown in Figure 3.18 (e). Since there are two lone pairs the bond angle is compressed even more, to around 104°. On forming H_3O^+ a pyramidal structure results, and in extremely acidic solution H_4O^{2+} forms, in small quantities, and is tetrahedral.

5 bond pairs

This is exemplified by gaseous PCl_5, three bonds are at 120° in a plane, with two others at 90° to this plane, giving the trigonal bipyramid shape shown in Figure 3.18(f).

Solid PCl_5 has a different structure, with tetrahedral PCl_4^+ and octahedral PCl_6^- ions.

3 bond pairs, 2 lone pairs

Where lone pairs are present among 5 electron pairs, the lone pairs always occupy the equatorial plane. Thus ClF_3 is T-shaped, with two lone pairs (Figure 3.18(g)).

6 bond pairs

All the bond angles are 90°, and the structure is a regular octahedron. This is found in SF_6, and in the huge number of hexacoordinated transition metal complexes, such as hexaquairon(II), $[Fe(H_2O)_6]^{2+}$ as shown in Figure 3.18(h).

Therefore all that needs to be known in order to predict shapes is the number of electron pairs that have to be accommodated, and it does not matter whether neutral molecules or ions are being considered. What has not been done here is to explain the mechanism by which the orbitals achieve these shapes; that lies outside our present concerns.

Metallic bonding

The principal physical characteristics of metals are their plastic nature (that is, they can be deformed without breaking), and their electrical conductivity, which is much greater than most non-metals but which shows quite wide variation within the metals themselves. These properties have to be explained by the bonding, which must be strong, not particularly directional, and must provide free charge carriers for the conductivity.

The outer electrons in metals are not paired up into individual bonds, but rather are free to move around the whole lattice structure of the metal which is formed from the positive ions. The free movement of this 'sea' of electrons allows for conductivity, and the non-directional nature of the bonds allows malleability. A good macroscopic analogy is that of a group of ball-bearings, representing the ions, covered in grease, representing the sea of electrons.

The best conductor is silver, followed by copper; other metals are much

Draw the following so as to show their shape. Give reasons for your choice.

(a) BCl_3; (b) PCl_3 (c) $BeCl_2$;
(d) CO_2 (e) NH_3; (f) $SnCl_2$;
(g) $SnCl_4$ (h) PCl_5 (i) SF_6
(j) PCl_6^-; (k) NO_2^-
(l) NO_2^+; (m) CO_3^{2-};
(n) SO_4^{2-}; (o) SO_2;
(p) SO_3^{2-}; (q) BrF_3;
(r) XeF_4; (s) BrF_4^-

poorer, and resistance wires, e.g. for electric fires, are made from alloys such as Ni/Cr (nichrome). Table 3.10 gives some values for the resistance of selected elements, relative to silver which is the best conductor there is, other than superconductors.

Table 3.10 *Resistances relative to silver of selected elements; nonmetals are shown in bold type*

Element	Ag	Cu	Fe	Pb	Ni	Cr	Hg	Au	C	Si	S
Relative resistance	1.0	1.05	6.2	13.5	4.3	7.9	65	1.5	887	10^{18}	$\sim 10^{23}$

The 'good conductor' graphite looks distinctly poor compared with even the poorest of the metals. The conductivity of graphite comes from the π-electrons which are delocalised over the sheets of hexagons which form its layer lattice, which is really a stack of giant molecules weakly bonded by van der Waals' forces. Since the electrons are mobile only along the layers, a single graphite crystal will conduct parallel to the sheets, but will not conduct at right angles to them.

4 Oxidation/reduction and the transition metals

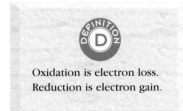

Oxidation and reduction

Oxidation and reduction are found with all but four elements in the Periodic Table, not just with the transition metals, although they show these reactions to such an extent that they could be accused of self-indulgence.

Definitions

When magnesium reacts with oxygen (Figure 4.1)

$$2Mg(s) + O_2(g) \rightarrow 2MgO(s)$$

the product contains Mg^{2+} and O^{2-} ions. Reaction with oxygen is pretty clearly oxidation! The reaction of magnesium with chlorine

$$Mg(s) + Cl_2(g) \rightarrow MgCl_2(g)$$

gives a compound with Mg^{2+} and Cl^- ions. In both cases the magnesium atom has lost electrons, so as far as the magnesium is concerned the reactions are the same. This idea is generalised into the definition of oxidation as loss of electrons. Reduction is therefore the gain of electrons. Since electrons don't vanish from the universe, oxidation and reduction occur together in **redox** reactions.

Oxidation numbers

For simple monatomic ions such as Fe^{2+} it's easy to see when they are oxidised (to Fe^{3+}) or reduced (to Fe). For ions such as NO_3^- or SO_3^{2-} which also undergo oxidation and reduction it is not always so easy to see what is happening in terms of electrons. To assist this, the idea of **oxidation number** or **oxidation state** is used. The two terms are usually used interchangeably, so that an ion may have a particular oxidation number or be in a particular oxidation state.

Each element in a compound is treated as though it is an ion, no matter what the actual nature of the bonding. If during a reaction the 'charge' on the 'ion' becomes more positive, then that part of the compound has been oxidised. The inverted commas are used because the compound may not be ionic; it is taken to be so for this electronic book-keeping exercise.

Some atoms have defined oxidation states. There are three simple rules to start with.

1 Elements have an oxidation number zero.
2 A simple monatomic ion has an oxidation number that is the same as its charge. The oxidation number is given in Arabic numerals with the appropriate sign, except when naming compounds, where Roman numerals are used. Thus Fe^{3+} is iron($+3$), but a compound of it would be, say, iron(III) chloride.

Figure 4.1 The use of magnesium flares in photography being demonstrated at an early meeting of the British Association in Birmingham (1865)

3 The oxidation number of hydrogen is (+1) in most of its compounds, and that of oxygen is (–2) (There are some exceptions to this which will be considered once the main rules are established.). Fluorine is always (–1).

To see how to use oxidation numbers, consider the reaction between chlorine and bromide ions. The oxidation numbers are shown underneath each substance:

$$Cl_2 + 2Br^- \rightarrow 2Cl^- + Br_2$$

(0)　　(–1)　　(–1)　　(0)

The chlorine has been reduced because its oxidation number has gone down; the bromide has been oxidised because its oxidation number has risen.

That example is simple enough to make the use of oxidation numbers unnecessary in such a formal way. However, consider the reaction of manganate(VII) ions with iron(II) ions:

$$MnO_4^-(aq) + 5Fe^{2+}(aq) + 8H^+(aq) \rightarrow Mn^{2+}(aq) + 5Fe^{3+}(aq) + 4H_2O(l).$$

It is easy enough to see that the iron(II) ions have been oxidised to iron(III), but not so easy to see why there are 5 of them for every MnO_4^-. If we use the oxidation number (–2) for oxygen, pretending that the manganate ion is wholly ionically bonded we get:

$$[Mn^{x+}(O^{2-})_4]^-$$

from which $x = 7$. Thus since the product is Mn^{2+}, there must have been five electrons added to the MnO_4^- to reduce it. These come from 5 Fe^{2+} ions, losing one electron each. The manganese in MnO_4^- is not actually a (7+) ion (indeed you will know from Topic 3 that such a highly charged ion would be so polarising as to give covalent bonding) but it behaves in redox reactions as though it is.

Another common reducing agent is dichromate(VI), $Cr_2O_7^{2-}$, which is not quite as powerful as manganate(VII). Using the same idea as before, in this case $[(Cr^{y+})_2(O^{2-})_7]^{2-}$, it is not hard to get $y = 6$. When dichromate(VI) is reduced, it forms two Cr^{3+} ions, a 6 electron change.

To see which part of a compound is negative and which is positive in finding oxidation numbers the electronegativity is used. The more electronegative atom has the negative oxidation number. So in ammonia, NH_3, nitrogen is the more electronegative and has oxidation number (–3); in nitrite, NO_2^-, it is (+3), and in nitrate, NO_3^-, (+5). Carbon in carbon dioxide, CO_2 is (+4), but in methane, CH_4, it is (–4) . This is because carbon is more electronegative than hydrogen. The oxidation number is not the same as an element's valency or combining power. Carbon shows valency four only.

Sometimes hydrogen does not have oxidation number (+1). In sodium hydride, NaH, it is combined with a less electronegative atom, and so hydrogen has the oxidation number (–1) in ionic hydrides. Oxygen shows positive oxidation numbers only when combined with fluorine, e.g. it is (+2) in oxygen difluoride, F_2O.

Compounds or ions which apparently show fractional oxidation numbers usually have atoms of the same type with two or more different oxidation numbers. In tri-iron tetroxide, Fe_3O_4, for example, there is one Fe(+2) and one Fe(+3), the oxide behaving as $FeO.Fe_2O_3$. In trilead tetroxide, Pb_3O_4, the compound behaves as $2PbO.PbO_2$, i.e. Pb(+2) and Pb(+4). The only exception to this is the superoxide ion O_2^-, with oxidation number for the oxygen of $(-\frac{1}{2})$.

Oxidation numbers and redox reactions

The usefulness of oxidation numbers lies largely in the derivation of equations for redox reactions. These always involve something being oxidised and something being reduced, and so can be split into two half reactions, one for the oxidation and one for the reduction. These are the processes which occur at the electrodes if the reaction is done in an electrochemical cell (Topic 17, Module 3). Knowing a few half-reactions means that you can combine them into a wide variety of full reactions since a given oxidising agent is, under given conditions, usually reduced in the same way whatever the reducing agent. You can learn about the exceptions to this if you go beyond 'A' level.

The oxidation of bromide ions by chlorine, mentioned earlier, affords a simple example. Chlorine is reduced to chloride:

$$Cl_2 + 2e^- \rightarrow 2Cl^-$$

and bromide is oxidised to bromine:

$$2Br^- \rightarrow Br_2 + 2e^-$$

Addition of these two half-reactions gives the full reaction

$$Cl_2 + 2Br^- \rightarrow Br_2 + 2Cl^-$$

The electrons given up by the bromide ions are the same electrons as those accepted by the chlorine atoms. When half-reactions are combined, the number of electrons in each must be the same, which may require one or both half-reactions to be multiplied by an integer. Note that a half-reaction cannot be written unless the starting and finishing substances are known; there is no general rule for deriving the product from the reagent.

Manganate(VII) ion in acid solution is reduced to Mn^{2+}:

$$MnO_4^- \rightarrow Mn^{2+}$$

but other things are clearly needed. Five electrons are required for the reduction from manganese(+7) to manganese(+2):

$$MnO_4^- + 5e^- \rightarrow Mn^{2+},$$

but there are still the four oxygens in the ion to deal with. Remembering that these are regarded as O^{2-}, they are converted to water with hydrogen ions:

Find the oxidation numbers of:
(a) Fe in FeCl
(b) Cl in NaCl
(c) S in SO_4^{2-};
(d) S in SO_3^{2-};
(e) Mn in MnO_4^{2-};
(f) Mn in MnO_2;
(g) C in CO;
(h) C in CO_2;
(i) C in CCl_4
(j) Cr in CrO_3;
(k) Os in OsO_4;
(l) Br in BrF_3;
(m) Cl in HOCl;
(n) Cl in $HCClO_3$;
(o) Cl in $HClO_4$;
(p) Fe in $[Fe(CN)_6]^{4-}$;
(q) Cu in $CuCl_4^{2-}$;
(r) O in F_2O.

$$MnO_4^- + 5e^- + 8H^+ \rightarrow Mn^{2+} + 4H_2O$$

This is the half-reaction for potassium manganate(VII) reduction in acid.

The half-reaction for oxidation of iron(II) to iron(III) is:

$$Fe^{2+} \rightarrow Fe^{3+} + e^-$$

and since 5 electrons are needed to reduce the manganate(VII) this equation is multiplied by 5 and then added to the MnO_4^- half-reaction to get

$$MnO_4^- + 5Fe^{2+} + 8H^+ \rightarrow Mn^{2+} + 5Fe^{3+} + 4H_2O$$

In general if O^{2-} needs to be disposed of from the left-hand side, H^+ will do it. With dichromate(VI),

$$Cr_2O_7^{2-} \quad + \quad 6e^- \quad + \quad 14H^+ \quad \rightarrow \quad 2Cr^{3+} \quad + \quad 7H_2O$$

$$\begin{array}{ll} \text{reducing} & \text{for } 7O^{2-} \\ 2 \times Cr(+6) \text{ to} & \\ 2 \times Cr(+3) & \end{array}$$

In many cases reducing agents require more oxygen, for instance when NO_2^- becomes NO_3^-. The need is for O^{2-}, which can be obtained from water, $2H^+$ remaining:

$$NO_2^- + H_2O \rightarrow NO_3^- + 2e^- + 2H^+$$

the $2e^-$ coming from the oxidation of N(+3) to N(+5). The electrons and hydrogen ions do not combine to form hydrogen, since the electrons aren't free but will have been given to the oxidising agent.

Suppose that the oxidising agent is manganate(VII). Writing the two half-reactions,

$$MnO_4^- + 8H^+ + 5e^- \rightarrow Mn^{2+} + 4H_2O$$

$$NO_2^- + H_2O \rightarrow NO_3^- + 2e^- + 2H^+$$

the electrons donated are made the same as the number of electrons received if we multiply the top half reaction by 2 and the bottom by 5,

$$2MnO_4^- + 16H^+ + 10e^- \rightarrow 2Mn^{2+} + 8H_2O$$

$$5NO_2^- + 5H_2O \rightarrow 5NO_3^- + 10e^- + 10H^+$$

We then add to get the overall reaction

$$2MnO_4^- + 5NO_2^- + 6H^+ \rightarrow 2Mn^{2+} + 5NO_3^- + 3H_2O$$

Consider one more example, the reaction of dichromate(VI) ion with hydrogen peroxide in acid solution. Hydrogen peroxide can behave both as a reducing agent, as here, or as an oxidising agent. The half-reactions are

OXIDATION/REDUCTION

$$Cr_2O_7^{2-} + 6e^- + 14H^+ \rightarrow 2Cr^{3+} + 7H_2O$$

$$H_2O_2 \rightarrow O_2 + 2H^+ + 2e^-$$

Multiplying the second equation by 3 and adding gives the overall reaction

$$Cr_2O_7^{2-} + 3H_2O_2 + 8H^+ \rightarrow 2Cr^{3+} + 3O_2 + 7H_2O$$

Using half reactions, large numbers of redox reactions can be derived which otherwise would have to be learnt individually. Table 4.1 gives some which should be known.

You should not pass over any redox reaction without writing out the half-reactions and being clear what the changes in the oxidation numbers are.

Table 4.1 *Some half-reactions*

$MnO_4^- + 8H^+ + 5e^- \rightarrow Mn^{2+} + 4H_2O$
$Cr_2O_7^{2-} + 14H^+ + 6e^- \rightarrow 2Cr^{3+} + 7H_2O$
$H_2O_2 \rightarrow O_2 + 2H^+ + 2e^-$ (reducing agent)
$H_2O_2 + 2H^+ + 2e^- \rightarrow 2H_2O$ (oxidising agent)
$NO_2^- + H_2O \rightarrow NO_3^- + 2H^+ + 2e^-$
$SO_3^{2-} + H_2O \rightarrow SO_4^{2-} + 2H^+ + 2e^-$
$2ClO_3^- + 12H^+ + 10e^- \rightarrow Cl_2 + 6H_2O$
$FeO_4^{2-} + 8H^+ + 3e^- \rightarrow Fe^{3+} + 4H_2O$
$2IO_3^- + 12H^+ + 10e^- \rightarrow I_2 + 6H_2O$
$MnO_2 + 4H^+ + 2e^- \rightarrow Mn^{2+} + 2H_2O$
$PbO_2 + 4H^+ + 2e^- \rightarrow Pb^{2+} + 2H_2O$
$2S_2O_3^{2-} \rightarrow S_4O_6^{2-} + 2e^-$
$VO^{2+} + 2H^+ + e^- \rightarrow V^{3+} + H_2O$
$VO_2^+ + 2H^+ + e^- \rightarrow VO^{2+} + H_2O$

Combine the required half-reactions from table 4.1 and elsewhere in this section to obtain the oxidation-reduction reactions between.

(a) MnO_4^- and H_2O_2;
(b) MnO_4^- and SO_3^{2-};
(c) MnO_4^- and NO_2^-;
(d) $Cr_2O_7^{2-}$ and H_2O_2;
(e) MnO_4^- and I^-;
(f) PbO_2 and Cl^-;
(g) V^{3+} and MnO_4^- (two reactions successively);
(h) $S_2O_3^{2-}$ and I_2;
(i) ClO_3^- and Cl^-.

Separate the following oxidation-reduction reactions into their two constituent half-reactions:

(a) $2FeCl_2 + Cl_2 \rightarrow 2FeCl_3$
(b) $2KBr + Cl_2 \rightarrow 2KCl + Br_2$
(c) $MnO_2 + 4HCl \rightarrow MnCl_2 + Cl_2 + 2H_2O$
(d) $MnO_4^- + 5Fe^{2+} + 8H^+ \rightarrow Mn^{2+} + 5Fe^{3+} + 4H_2O$
(e) $2MnO_4^- + 5C_2O_4^{2-} + 16H^+ \rightarrow 2Mn^{2+} + 5CO_2 + 8H_2O$
(f) $2S_2O_3^{2-} + I_2 \rightarrow S_4O_6^{2-} + 2I^-$
(g) $H_2SO_4 + 8HI \rightarrow H_2S + 4I_2 + 4H_2O$
(h) $IO_3^- + 5I^- + 6H^+ \rightarrow 3I_2 + 3H_2O$
(i) $Cu^{2+} + 2I^- \rightarrow CuI + I_2$
(j) $Zn + Cu^{2+} \rightarrow Zn^{2+} + Cn$
(k) $Fe_2O_3 + 2Al \rightarrow Al_2O_3 + 2Fe$
(m) $KIO_3 + 2Na_2SO_3 \rightarrow KIO + 2Na_2SO_4$
(n) $Sn + 4HNO_3 \rightarrow SnO_2 + 4NO_2 + 2H_2O$
(o) $Cl_2 + 2NaOH \rightarrow NaCl + NaOCl + H_2O$
(p) $2H_2O_2 \rightarrow 2H_2O + O_2$

The transition metals

The d-block and transition metals

The d-block of the Periodic Table is that set of elements in which the d-shell is being filled; we shall consider only the first series from scandium element 21, to zinc, element 30. Within these 10 elements lie the eight of the first transition series, titanium to copper.

Redox or oxidation/reduction reactions are a significant part of the chemistry of the transition elements.

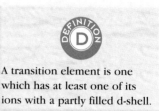

A transition element is one which has at least one of its ions with a partly filled d-shell.

The aufbau principle (Chapter 1) shows that the 3d subshell fills after the 4s, which is complete at element 20, calcium $1s^2 2s^2 2p^6 3s^2 3p^6 4s^2$ or $[Ar]4s^2$. Scandium is therefore $[Ar]3d^1 4s^2$, and zinc at the other end of the series is $[Ar]3d^{10}4s^2$. Neither scandium nor zinc are transition metals since the only ion scandium forms is Sc^{3+}, with no d electrons, and zinc forms only Zn^{2+} ($3d^{10}$), with a full d subshell.

Transition metals are so-called because their properties are transitional between those of the strongly electropositive metals of the s-block and the less metallic and non-metallic elements in the p-block. Because the orbital being filled is an inner one, the change in chemistry across the series is less marked than the change which is seen across a similar number of elements in the main groups, where electrons are being added to the outermost orbital. In transition metals the increase in nuclear charge is offset to a large extent by increased screening of the outer electrons, so ionisation energies do not vary very much, nor do atomic radii. Vertical trends are much less significant than those in main groups, especially in those transition metal groups which do not have the same valence shell electron structures. Unlike main group elements there is often some variation in the $(n-1)dns$ electronic configuration, seen at its most extreme in nickel, $3d^8 4s^2$, palladium, $4d^{10}$, and platinum, $5d^9 6s^1$. Horizontal trends are more important. The second and third transition series are left to more advanced work.

Electron structures and variable oxidation numbers

First series transition metal electron structures are given in Table 4.2, the 3d4s orbitals being used. There are energy advantages in having the d orbitals half-full or full, and this is the reason for the unexpected structures for Cr and Cu. This is a good example of apparently small differences giving rise to considerable changes in the chemistry which was mentioned in Chapter 1. Such half-shell stability is also responsible for some transition metal ions being favoured over others, e.g. Fe^{3+} (d^5) over Fe^{2+} (d^6).

Table 4.2 *Electronic configurations in the d-block*

	Sc	Ti	V	Cr	Mn	Fe	Co	Ni	Cu	Zn
3d	1	2	3	5	5	6	7	8	10	10
4s	2	2	2	1	2	2	2	2	1	2

Owing to increasing nuclear charge the atomic radii fall between calcium and chromium. Further addition of electrons to the 3d then makes relatively little difference, with size rising slowly because of increased screening of the outer electrons from the nucleus, until there is a significant rise at zinc. Figure 4.2 shows the metallic radii.

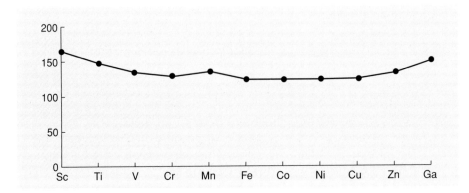

Figure 4.2 Metallic radii/pm, for the first transition series

The same gradual trend is seen for first and second ionisation energies (Figure 4.3), in complete contrast to the trends in main group elements.

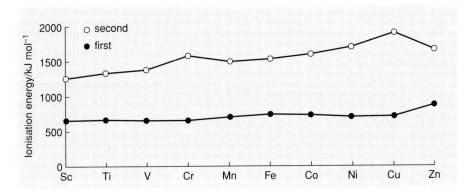

Figure 4.3 First and second ionisation energies in the first transition series

Successive ionisation energies for a given atom rise by a similar amount each time, until there is a large jump when all 4s and 3d electrons have been removed. Figure 4.4 shows successive ionisation energies for vanadium and for copper.

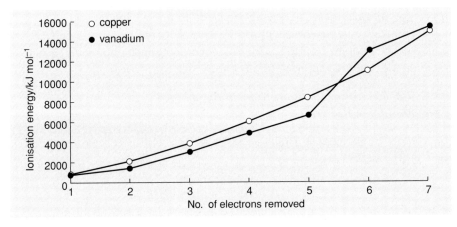

Figure 4.4 Successive ionisation energies for vanadium and copper

The increases between successive ionisation energies are compensated for by increased bond strengths or increased hydration enthalpy of the ions, enabling the transition metal to have several oxidation numbers. However the various balances between the energies of one oxidation number and another are not usually obvious, so that the explanations of 'preference' for one over another can look distinctly like special pleading, and in fact careful calculation of all the contributing factors, some of which are very subtle, is required. This is not exclusively a transition metal property, the heavier metals in Groups 3, 4 and 5 also show this feature, but not to the same extent.

Variable valency is one of the distinguishing features of transition metal chemistry. The other main characteristics are the formation of complex ions, the formation of coloured ions, paramagnetism in ions and catalytic activity in both elements and compounds. These will now be considered further.

Formation of complex ions

Complex ions consist of a metal ion surrounded by a number, commonly six in an octahedral arrangement, of **ligands**. These ligands are molecules or ions which are bonded covalently to the transition metal ion by donation of lone pairs of electrons into empty metal orbitals. The transition metal's d electrons are not involved in this ligand bonding In octahedral complexes the ligands may use the two 3d orbitals, $d_{x^2-y^2}$ and d_{z^2}, which point towards the ligands (see Figure 1.15) if these orbitals are unoccupied, together with as many as are necessary of unoccupied 4s, 4p and 4d orbitals which are low enough in energy to receive the ligand lone pairs. An example is the ion hexaquairon(II), $[Fe(H_2O)_6]^{2+}$, for which an electrons-in-boxes diagram can be drawn as shown in Figure 4.5.

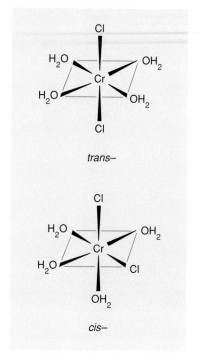

Figure 4.6 Some complexes of chromium(III)

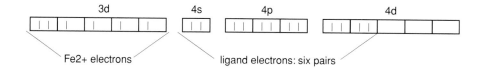

Figure 4.5 Electron arrangement in the hexaquairon(II) ion

Octahedral complexes are commonest, and ions such as $[Cr(H_2O)_6]^{3+}$, $[Fe(H_2O)_6]^{2+}$, and $[Cu(H_2O)_6]^{2+}$ are found in solutions often referred to simply as $Cr^{3+}(aq)$, $Fe^{2+}(aq)$ and $Cu^{2+}(aq)$. The complexes with water ligands are called aqua or aquo complexes. The ligands do not all have to be the same; $Cr(+3)$ forms a series of compounds with the formula $CrCl_3.6H_2O$, that is $[Cr(H_2O)_6]^{3+}.3Cl^-$; $[Cr(H_2O)5Cl]^{2+}.2Cl^-.H_2O$, $[Cr(H_2O)4Cl_2]^+.Cl^-.2H_2O$. The last of these has two isomers, *cis* and *trans*, the names referring to the position of the chloride ligands (Figure 4.6). Isomerism is not confined to organic chemistry!

Coloured ions

Transition metal ions are coloured because they absorb light in certain parts of the visible spectrum, the observed colour being the remainder which is transmitted or reflected. The absorbed light causes electron transitions of two types

Transitions between one subset of the d orbitals and another

In an octahedral complex, three of the d-orbitals, which do not point towards the ligands, are at a lower energy than the other two, which do, and which are repelled by the electron density in the ligands if the metal orbitals are occupied. They will be in ions with four or more d electrons; otherwise the empty orbital can accept ligand electrons. Either way, the energy of the d_{xy}, d_{yz} and d_{xy} orbitals is lower than that of the other two.

The colours absorbed are quite broad in wavelength range, because the metal–ligand distance, and hence the energy splitting of the orbitals, varies due to thermal vibrations. This therefore varies the colour of the light absorbed.

Electron transitions between the lower and upper levels absorb energy as visible light. The amount of energy depends on the ligands, so changing these will change the colour of the ion. Thus $[Cu(H_2O)_6]^{2+}$ is pale blue, whereas $[Cu(NH_3)_4(H_2O)_2]^{2+}$ is very deep blue. Cu^+ is a d^{10} ion which has no spaces for electron transitions, and is colourless.

Transitions between the central metal ion and atoms covalently bonded to it

The covalently bonded atoms are usually oxygen. The metal has a high oxidation number (see below), and the ions are strongly coloured. Examples include manganate(VII), MnO_4^- and dichromate(VI), $Cr_2O_7^{2-}$. Both $Mn(+7)$ and $Cr(+6)$ are formally d^0 ions, and so cannot show the d–d transitions mentioned above.

Paramagnetism in ions

Paramagnetic substances are weakly attracted in to a magnetic field. This is the result of unpaired electrons which many transition metal ions possess. The extent of the attraction depends on the number of such electrons, and gives useful information on electron distributions in complex ions.

The action of alkali on aqua complexes

Solutions of sodium hydroxide or ammonia are used in the qualitative analysis of transition metal ions, and the reactions illustrate some of their properties.

Aqua ions of transition metals are acidic. The water ligands are strongly polarised by the electron-withdrawing effect of the small highly-charged metal

Draw electrons-in-boxes diagrams for
(a) $[Cu(H_2O)_6]^{2+}$,
(b) $[Cr(H_2O)_4Cl_2]^+$..

Why are scandium(III) compounds colourless?

ion, so protons are removed in a nucleophilic attack by the solvent water. For hexaquairon(III) the following reaction takes place:

This equilibrium can be moved further to the right by adding hydroxide ions, which are much more basic than water and so therefore much better at deprotonating the complex. The result is that the metal hydroxide precipitates;

The colours of the precipitates (Table 4.3) can be used to identify the ions. The reaction is the same whether the hydroxide ion comes from sodium hydroxide or from ammonia solution via the reaction

$$NH_3(aq) + H_2O(l) \quad NH_4^+(aq) + OH^-(aq).$$

In this reaction water is acting as an acid, donating the protons to the ammonia. Whether water acts as acid or base depends on the acid or base strength of the other substance (Topic 8, Module 2).

Many transition metal ions react further if more alkali is added. The reactions are often different for sodium hydroxide and ammonia. Since sodium hydroxide is a strong base, further reaction depends on the metal hydroxide also having acidic properties as well at its expected basic ones, i.e. it must be amphoteric. Chromium(III) hydroxide is an example of such an oxide. It reacts as a base with aqueous acid,

$$Cr(OH)_3(s) + 3H^+(aq) \rightarrow Cr^{3+}(aq) + 3H_2O(l)$$

and as an acid with aqueous base,

$$Cr(OH)_3(s) + 3OH^-(aq) \rightarrow [Cr(OH)_6]^{3-}(aq)$$

The result is a deep-green solution of the ion $[Cr(OH)_6]^{3-}$. Addition of acid deprotonates this and it reverts to $Cr(OH)_3$ with the green precipitate reappearing.

Ammonia is too weak a base for the amphoteric hydroxides to react as acids.

Suppose you have solutions of $[Fe(H_2O)_6]^{2+}$ and $[Fe(H_2O)_6]^{3+}$, of equal molar concentration. Which would be more acidic, and why?

Suggest how, using either sodium hydroxide solution or ammonia solution as appropriate, you could separate the ions in aqueous solutions of
(a) Zn^{2+} and Cu^{2+};
(b) Fe^{2+} and Cr^{3+}.

OXIDATION/REDUCTION

Some transition metals will instead form complexes with the ammonia as ligand, such complexes being soluble. Copper(II) provides a good example; with ammonia a pale blue gelatinous precipitate of copper(II) hydroxide, $Cu(OH)_2$, appears; with excess ammonia this reacts to give a wonderfully deep blue, soluble complex. The nature of this depends rather on one's interpretation of copper chemistry. Some regard the complex as a square planar with four ammonia ligands, others as octahedral with two water ligands in addition. Taking the latter view, the reaction is

$$Cu(OH)_2(s) + 4NH_3(aq) + 2H_2O(l) \rightarrow [Cu(NH_3)_4(H_2O)_2]^{2+}(aq) + 2OH^-(aq)$$

The reaction is a **ligand exchange**.

Table 4.3 summarises some reactions of ions from the first transition series. The equations should be known, together with the observations. For convenience the aqua ions are usually written, for instance, as $Cr^{3+}(aq)$ rather than $[Cr(H_2O)_6]^{3+}$, but remember that the ligands are there.

Write out a similar sequence of reactions (in full) to those showing deprotonation of $[Fe(H_2O)_6]^{3+}$ by aqueous hydroxide ions, but using $[Cu(H_2O)_6]^{2+}$ as your example.

Table 4.3 *Reactions of transition metal ions with sodium hydroxide and ammonia. All reactions are in aqueous solution, so (aq) is omitted. The transition metal ions are hexaquo species $[M(H_2O)_6]^{n+}$*

Ion	with NaOH or NH3 not in excess	With NaOH in excess	With NH₃ in excess
Ti^{4+}	$Ti^{4+} + 4OH^- \rightarrow Ti(OH)_4$. White precipitate	No further reaction	No further reaction
V^{2+}	$V^{2+} + 2OH^- \rightarrow V(OH)_2$. Violet precipitate	No further reaction	No further reaction
V^{3+}	$2V^{3+} + 6OH^- \rightarrow V_2O_3 + 3H_2O$. Green precipitate	No further reaction	No further reaction
Cr^{3+}	$Cr^{3+} + 3OH^- \rightarrow Cr(OH)_3$. Green precipitate	$Cr(OH)_3 + 3OH^- \rightarrow [Cr(OH)_6]^{3-}$. Deep green solution	No further reaction
Mn^{2+}	$Mn^{2+} + 2OH^- \rightarrow Mn(OH)_2$. Buff precipitate which darkens in air as MnO_2 forms	No further reaction	No further reaction
Fe^{2+}	$Fe^{2+} + 2OH^- \rightarrow Fe(OH)^2$. Dirty green precipitate which turns brown at surface due to oxidation to $Fe(OH)_3$ with air	No further reaction	No further reaction
Fe^{3+}	$Fe^{3+} + 3OH^- \rightarrow Fe(OH)_3$. Foxy-red precipitate	No further reaction	No further reaction
Co^{2+}	$Co^{2+} + 2OH^- \rightarrow Co(OH)_2$. Blue ppt which turns brown in air as $Co(OH)_3$ is formed	No further reaction	$Co(OH)_2 + 6NH_3 \rightarrow [Co(NH_3)_6]^{2+} + 2OH^-$. Blue solutions which oxidise in air to $[Co(NH_3)_6]^{3+}$
Ni^{2+}	$Ni^{2+} + 2OH^- \rightarrow Ni(OH)_2$. Pale green precipitate	No further reaction	$Ni(OH)_2 + 6NH_3 \rightarrow [Ni(NH_3)_6]^{2+} + 2OH^-$. Pale lavender-blue solution
Cu^{2+}	$Cu^{2+} + 2OH^- \rightarrow Cu(OH)_2$. Pale blue precipitate	No further reaction, although the precipitate is appreciably soluble	$Cu(OH)_2 + 4NH_3 + 2H_2O \rightarrow [Cu(NH_3)_4(H_2O)_2]^{2+} + 2OH^-$. Deep blue solution

Vanadium

Vanadium is not a common metal and there are no large-scale ore deposits. However, it is useful in alloy steels which are subject to shock and which need to be springy, for example for making spanners, and vanadium(V) oxide, V_2O_5, is used in the Contact Process for manufacture of sulphuric acid, as the catalyst for the oxidation of sulphur dioxide to sulphur trioxide.

It is easy to show the interconversion of the various oxidation states of vanadium and the colours are pretty (Table 4.4).

Table 4.4 *Some compounds of vanadium*

Oxidation state	d-shell	Common ion in water	Other compounds
V(+5)	0	yellow, VO_2^+,	VF_5, VO_3^-, V_2O_5
V(+4)	1	blue, VO^{2+}	VCl_4, VO_2
V(+3)	2	green, $[V(H_2O)_6]^{3+}$	V_2O_3
V(+2)	3	lavender, $[V(H_2O)_6]^{2+}$	

V(+5) is mildly oxidising, V(+4) is the most stable state in presence of air, V(+3) the most stable in absence of air, and V(+2) is strongly reducing.

Ammonium metavanadate, NH_4VO_3 is a colourless solid which dissolves in acid to give a yellow solution of VO_2^+. Addition of zinc powder and shaking produces successively green (VO_2^+ and VO^{2+}), blue (VO^{2+}), green (V^{3+}) and lavender (V^{2+}).

Vanadium (V) exists only with fluorine or oxygen, for instance as VF_5 and V_2O_5. The species in aqueous solution vary with pH, being VO_2^+ at pH 1, $V_5O_{14}^{3-}$ just below pH 7, and VO_4^{3-} above pH 12. You do not need to remember these complexities. V_2O_5 is a brown solid, is quite acidic, and is used as a catalyst.

Vanadium(IV) can be produced by mild reduction of vanadium(V), for example with aqueous sulphur dioxide:

$$2VO_2^+(aq) + SO_3^{2-}(aq) + 2H^+(aq) \rightarrow 2VO^{2+}(aq) + SO_4^{2-}(aq) + H_2O(l)$$

Justify the view that vanadium is a transition metal, giving examples of the characteristic properties you would expect.

Write the half-reactions for
the two redox reactions of
VO_2^+ shown.

or with iron(II):

$$VO_2^+(aq) + Fe^{2+}(aq) + 2H^+(aq) \rightarrow VO^{2+}(aq) + Fe^{3+}(aq) + H_2O(l)$$

Vanadium(III) needs more powerful reducing agents for its production than does vanadium(IV), and is readily oxidised by air. Further reduction to vanadium(II) is quite slow, and although a number of vanadium(II) compounds are known, the aqueous solution is strongly reducing and will even react with solvent water if no other oxidising agent is available:

$$2V^{2+}(aq) + 2H_2O(l) \rightarrow 2V^{3+}(aq) + H_2(g) + 2OH^-(aq)$$

Iron

Iron is the second most abundant metal in the earth's crust (aluminium is the most abundant), and its engineering importance hardly needs comment here. The importance of carbon and its oxides in the extraction of iron is covered in Topic 21 of Module 3 (Figure 4.7).

Iron is usually used in mild steel, an alloy with about 0.5% carbon. It oxidises very readily in the presence of water and oxygen to give the highest common oxidation state of iron as iron(III) oxide. Rust is the hydrated form of this, and it flakes off the surface exposing fresh metal to corrosion (Topic 21, Module 3).

Iron(III) is marginally the most stable state in air. The electron structure is $[Ar]3d^5$, and the ion is stabilised by the half-full, and therefore symmetrical, d-shell. Apart from rust, which commercially is the most significant iron(III) compound, the chloride, $FeCl_3$, is important, and exists in anhydrous and hydrated forms.

Anhydrous iron(III) chloride is a nearly black covalent solid. The Fe^{3+} ion is quite small and polarising enough to give a covalent compound with chlorine. Dimerisation to Fe_2Cl_6 occurs, and $FeCl_3$ can be used as a catalyst in the Friedel-Crafts reaction (Module 4, Topic 23) in the same way as $AlCl_3$ which also forms dimers.

Iron(III)chloride is made by synthesis, that is direct combination of the elements. Dry chlorine is passed over heated iron, (Figure 4.11), and the product sublimes into the cooler receiver .

$$2Fe(s) + 3Cl_2(g) \rightarrow 2FeCl_3(s)$$

Iron(III) chloride dissolves in water rather slowly to give yellow solutions from which the hydrated salt $FeCl_3.6H_2O$ can be crystallised. This is used to etch "printed" circuit boards in electronics, where unprotected copper is oxidised:

$$Cu(s) + 2Fe^{3+}(aq) \rightarrow Cu^{2+}(aq) + 2Fe^{2+}(aq).$$

If Fe^{3+} solutions are made very acidic (pH < 0), the colour changes to amethyst; this is seen nicely in the double salt ammonium iron(III) sulphate, and in amethysts themselves which consist of quartz with iron(III) impurity.

Figure 4.7 A blast furnace

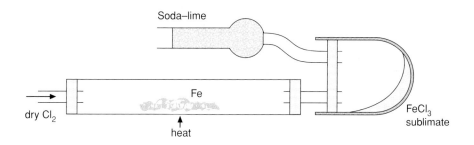

Figure 4.8 Synthesis of anhydrous iron(III) chloride

Hexaquairon(III), $[Fe(H_2O)_6]^{3+}$, is quite acidic, and more so than the hexaquairon(II) complex. It is deprotonated by sodium hydroxide or aqueous ammonia to give a foxy-red precipitate of iron(III) hydroxide, $Fe(OH)_3$, which does not react further with either reagent.

Anhydrous iron(II) chloride, $FeCl_2$, is white, and is made in a similar fashion to $FeCl_3$ except that hydrogen chloride gas is used. This is a weaker oxidising agent than chlorine, and the reaction is as follows:

$$Fe(s) + 2HCl(g) \rightarrow FeCl_2(s) + H_2(g).$$

With water, $FeCl_2$ gives a pale green solution of $[Fe(H_2O)_6]^{2+}$, which always contains traces of iron(III) owing to atmospheric oxidation, although making the solution acidic slows this considerably. Addition of sodium hydroxide or aqueous ammonia precipitates dirty-green iron(II) hydroxide, $Fe(OH)_2$, which does not react further with the reagents but will oxidise quite quickly in air to $Fe(OH)_3$ and turn foxy red.

A useful analytical test for iron ions is to use an iron complex with cyanide; for Fe^{3+} use the iron(II) complex $[Fe(CN)_6]^{4-}$, for iron(II) use $[Fe(CN)_6]^{3-}$. In both cases you get an intensely (and beautifully) blue precipitate. The test is very sensitive. Prussian blue was used by the Prussian army to colour their uniforms, for printing engineering blueprints, and for the locomotives of the Somerset & Dorset Joint Railway until 1923.

Catalytic activity and the transition elements

Catalysis is covered fully in Module 2, Topic 9, but the importance of transition metals and their compounds as catalysts necessitates a brief consideration here.

A catalyst increases the rate of a chemical reaction, but is not consumed in the process. It works by providing an alternative mechanism for the reaction to the uncatalysed one, with a lower energy barrier to be overcome. There are two types, homogeneous where the catalyst is in the same physical state as the reactants (gas, liquid, solution), and heterogeneous, where it is not. Heterogeneous catalysts are usually solids catalysing gas or liquid phase reactions.

Transition metal ions can function as homogeneous catalysts because they can

A sample of iron weighing 1.50 g was dissolved in dilute sulphuric acid, and the volume made to 250 cm^3. Portions of 25.0 cm^3 of the solution were titrated with 0.020 mol dm^{-3} potassium manganate(VII) solution, 26.4 cm^3 being required. Calculate the percentage purity of the iron.

Write equations to show
(a) the reduction of iron(III)oxide to iron using carbon monoxide,
(b) the reduction of iron(III)oxide to iron using carbon. Both reactions occur in the blast furnace.

Suggest a formula for Prussian Blue. It contains Fe, C and N only.

OXIDATION/REDUCTION

Write the equation for the oxidation of Fe^{2+}(aq) to Fe^{3+}(aq) using oxygen. The half-reaction for the reduction of oxygen is:

$$O_2 + 4H^+ + Fe^- \rightarrow 2H_2O$$

move between different oxidation states. An example (not of much industrial significance) is the slow reaction between cerium (IV), Ce^{4+} and thallium(I), Tl^+:

$$2Ce^{4+}(aq) + Tl^+(aq) \rightarrow 2Ce^{3+}(aq) + Tl^{3+}(aq).$$

This is catalysed by Mn^{2+} ions, their action is thought to be due to their ability to form Mn(III) and Mn(IV). Cerium(IV) oxidises manganese(II) successively to manganese(III) and manganese(IV). This then oxidises the thallium(I) ion, and reverts to manganese(II):

$$Ce^{4+} + Mn^{2+} \rightarrow Ce^{3+} + Mn^{3+}$$

$$Mn^{3+} + Ce^{4+} \rightarrow Ce^{3+} + Mn^{4+}$$

$$Mn^{4+} + Tl^+ \rightarrow Tl^{3+} + Mn^{2+}$$

Heterogeneous catalysis involves the combination of the reactants with the catalyst surface in some way. This weakens the bonds within the reactants, allowing them to form the products which then leave the catalyst surface. The exact sequence of events is complex, and depends on the strength of the bonds in the reactants and of those formed with the catalyst surface, as well as the size of the atoms in the lattice of the catalyst and the orbitals which it can make available to bond with the reactants. These must not bond strongly with the products. Thus a substance fulfilling all these requirements for a given reaction will not be common, and will probably not work for another reaction. Catalysts are usually specific to particular reactions.

Table 4.5 gives details of some industrially important catalysed reactions.

Table 4.5 *Industrially important catalysed reaction*

Process	Reaction	Catalyst and conditions
Haber: synthesis of ammonia	$3H_2(g) + N_2(g) \rightarrow 2NH_3(g)$	Iron with traces of potassium and aluminium oxides; 350–1000 atmospheres, 350°
Hydrogenation of alkenes: used in manufacture of margarine	$RCH{=}CHR' + H_2 \rightarrow RCH_2CH_2R'$	Platinum or palladium at room temperature (both very expensive); nickel at 50–150° (used commercially)
Contact: manufacture of sulphuric acid	$2SO_2(g) + O_2(g) \rightarrow 2SO_3(g)$	Vanadium (V) oxide, V_2O_5; 1.5 atmospheres 400°C. Platinum is good too, but expensive and easily poisoned by impurity in feed gases
Ostwald: oxidation of ammonia in manufacture of nitric acid	$4NH_3(g) + 5O_2(g) \rightarrow 4NO(g) + 6H_2O(g)$ NO reacts further with air to NO_2, which is then reacted with water	Platinum-rhodium alloy in form of a gauze; 900°C
Sandmeyer reaction	$C_6H_5N_2^+ + Cl^- \rightarrow C_6H_5Cl + N_2$	Copper(I) chloride
Ziegler-Natta polymerisation of alkenes	e.g. $CH_2{=}CH_2 \rightarrow$ polymer with highly controlled structure	complex of $TiCl_3$ and $Al(C_2H_5)_3$; various conditions depending on desired product

The Periodic Table

The Mendeleyev table

The Periodic Table is a great unifying idea in chemistry. It can tell you a lot about the chemistry of an element, and when it first appeared it fulfilled one of the greatest requirements of any discovery: not only did it bring together things already known, but enabled predictions, in this case about elements then unknown.

D.I. Mendeleyev (Figure 5.1) was not the first to attempt an arrangement of the elements, but when he published his table in 1869 he was clever (or daft) enough firstly to order the elements by atomic 'weight' (i.e. atomic mass) but was prepared to ignore the result if it clearly didn't work in terms of the known chemistry; and secondly left gaps for elements yet to be discovered.

Figure 5.1 Mendeleyev

Mendeleyev didn't have atomic numbers, the particles in the atom and its structure not being completely discovered for another 70 years or so. The use of relative atomic masses would have given a table with some anomalies, such as iodine being in Group 6 and tellurium in 7, which is absurd in chemical terms. Mendeleyev ignored the masses and stuck by the chemistry. Only after the work of Bohr and his colleagues on electronic structure (Chapter 1) was it clear that electronic structures determine the chemistry of an element, and that the atomic number orders the table. The 'anomaly' arose because relative atomic mass does not always increase with increase of atomic number.
The gaps were a triumph for the predictive powers of the table. Mendeleyev predicted ten elements, eight of which are now known. One does not exist since there is no gap in modern tables, and the other has a very high mass and the table does not (yet) go that far. The predictions he made for 'eka-silicon', now known as germanium, and its compounds, are shown in Table 5.1.

The arrangement by atomic number brings the elements into groups and periods, and the long form of the table shown in Figure 5.2 is the one with which you will doubtless be familiar. The atomic numbers are shown. The variation in electron configuration up to krypton is given in Table 5.2, which is the same as Table 1.4.

Aspects of the chemistry of Period 3, sodium to chlorine

The ideas of electronegativity, size and bond type of atoms which were covered in Topic 3 are illustrated well by the elements of the third period. The reactions which are used to illustrate trends can be used for any period in the Periodic Table.

THE PERIODIC TABLE

Table 5.1 *A comparison of eka-silicon and germanium*

Property	Predicted for eka-silicon, Es*	Actual for germanium, Ge
Relative atomic mass	72	72.6
Density	$5.5\,\mathrm{g\,cm^{-3}}$	$5.35\,\mathrm{g\,cm^{-3}}$
Colour	dirty grey	greyish-white
Reactions		
Air	burns on heating to white EsO_2	burns on heating to white GeO_2
Steam	reacts with difficulty	no reaction
Acids	slight reaction	no reaction
Alkalis	no reaction	only reacts if alkali is molten
Preparation	action of Na on K_2EsF_6	action of Na on K_2GeF_6
Properties of oxide	high T_m, density $4.7\,\mathrm{g\,cm^{-3}}$, weakly basic	high T_m, density $4.703\,\mathrm{g\,cm^{-3}}$, weakly basic
Properties of chloride	$EsCl_4$ liquid, $T_b < 100°C$, density $1.9\,\mathrm{g\,cm^{-3}}$.	$GeCl_4$ liquid $T_b = 83°C$, density $1.879\,\mathrm{g\,cm^{-3}}$.

*Es is now used for element 99, einsteinium

1 H	2 He

3 Li	4 Be											5 B	6 C	7 N	8 O	9 F	10 Ne
11 Na	12 Mg											13 Al	14 Si	15 P	16 S	17 Cl	18 Ar
19 K	20 Ca	21 Sc	22 Ti	23 V	24 Cr	25 Mn	26 Fe	27 Co	28 Ni	29 Cu	30 Zn	31 Ga	32 Ge	33 As	34 Se	35 Br	36 Kr
37 Rb	38 Sr	39 Y	40 Zr	41 Nb	42 Mo	43 Tc	44 Ru	45 Rh	46 Pd	47 Ag	48 Cd	49 In	50 Sn	51 Sb	52 Te	53 I	54 Xe
55 Cs	56 Ba	57 La	72 Hf	73 Ta	74 W	75 Re	76 Os	77 Ir	78 Pt	79 Au	80 Hg	81 Tl	82 Pb	83 Bi	84 Po	85 At	86 Rn
87 Fr	88 Ra	89 Sc															

58 Ce	59 Pr	60 Nd	61 Pm	62 Sm	63 Eu	64 Gd	65 Tb	66 Dy	67 Ho	68 Er	69 Tm	70 Yb	71 Lu
90 Th	91 Pa	92 U	93 Np	94 Pu	95 Am	96 Cm	97 Bk	98 Cf	99 Es	100 Fm	101 Md	102 No	103 Lr

Figure 5.2 The Periodic Table

Reactions of the elements

The reactions with oxygen, water and chlorine, summarised in Tables 5.3 – 5.5 are of most significance because oxygen and water are plentiful in the atmosphere, and chlorine is a typical strong oxidising agent.

Table 5.2 *Electron structures of the first 36 elements*

Atomic number	symbol	1s	2s	2p	3s	3p	3d	4s	4p
1	H	1							
2	He	2							
3	Li	2	1						
4	Be	2	2						
5	B	2	2	1					
6	C	2	2	2					
7	N	2	2	3					
8	O	2	2	4					
9	F	2	2	5					
10	Ne	2	2	6					
11	Na	2	2	6	1				
12	Mg	2	2	6	2				
13	Al	2	2	6	2	1			
14	Si	2	2	6	2	2			
15	P	2	2	6	2	3			
16	S	2	2	6	2	4			
17	Cl	2	2	6	2	5			
18	Ar	2	2	6	2	6			
19	K	2	2	6	2	6		1	
20	Ca	2	2	6	2	6		2	
21	Sc	2	2	6	2	6	1	2	
22	Ti	2	2	6	2	6	2	2	
23	V	2	2	6	2	6	3	2	
24	Cr	2	2	6	2	6	5	1	
25	Mn	2	2	6	2	6	5	2	
26	Fe	2	2	6	2	6	6	2	
27	Co	2	2	6	2	6	7	2	
28	Ni	2	2	6	2	6	8	2	
29	Cu	2	2	6	2	6	10	1	
30	Zn	2	2	6	2	6	10	2	
31	Ga	2	2	6	2	6	10	2	1
32	Ge	2	2	6	2	6	10	2	2
33	As	2	2	6	2	6	10	2	3
34	Se	2	2	6	2	6	10	2	4
35	Br	2	2	6	2	6	10	2	5
36	Kr	2	2	6	2	6	10	2	6

The electropositive metals (Na and Mg) with low ionisation energies and fairly large ions give ionic products. Aluminium has a small ion with high charge and is quite polarising, so the oxide is ionic but the chloride is covalent since the chloride ion is larger and so more polarisable than the oxide ion. The non-metals react with varying vigour to give covalent products as would be expected from their high ionisation energies and small size.

Table 5.3 *Reactions of the elements of Period 3 with oxygen*

Na	Tarnishes in air; burns with yellow flame on heating to give a mixture of the oxide and peroxide, a yellowish-white solid.
	$4Na\ (s) + O_2(g) \rightarrow 2Na_2O(s)$ and $2Na(s) + O_2(g) \rightarrow Na_2O_2(s)$
Mg	Superficial oxidation at room temperature, burns with brilliant white flame on heating. Oxide white, ionic.
	$2Mg(s) + O_2(g) \rightarrow 2MgO(s)$
Al	Superficial oxide layer forms at room temperature, which protects against further attack except by concentrated alkali, and enables the use of this relatively reactive metal for engineering purposes. Burns on heating in oxygen to give white, ionic oxide
	$4Al(s) + 3O_2(g) \rightarrow 2Al_2O_3(s)$
Si	No reaction at room temperature. Burns on heating in oxygen to give white, giant covalent oxide.
	$Si(s) + O_2(g) \rightarrow SiO_2(g)$
P	White phosphorus catches fire spontaneously in air, red phosphorus burns on heating, to give the white, covalent oxide.
	$P_4(s) + 5O_2(g) \rightarrow P_4O_{10}(s)$
S	Burns with bright blue flame on heating in air or oxygen, giving colourless covalent gaseous oxide.
	$S(s) + O_2(g) \rightarrow SO_2(g)$
Cl	Does not react directly with oxygen

Table 5.4 *Reactions of the elements of Period 3 with chlorine*

Na	Reacts on heating to give white, ionic chloride.
	$2Na(s) + Cl_2(g) \rightarrow 2NaCl(g)$
Mg	Reacts on heating to give white, ionic chloride.
	$Mg(s) + Cl_2(g) \rightarrow MgCl_2(s)$
Al	Reacts on heating to give pale-yellow, covalent dimeric chloride.
	$2Al(s) + 3Cl_2(g) \rightarrow Al_2Cl_6(s)$
Si	Reacts on heating to give colourless, covalent liquid chloride.
	$Si(s) + 2Cl_2(g) \rightarrow SiCl_4(l)$
P	Reacts on heating to give colourless, covalent liquid trichloride.
	$2P(s) + 3Cl_2(g) \rightarrow 2PCl_3(l)$
	Excess chlorine oxidises this product to a white solid containing PCl_4^+ and PCl_6^- ions; in the gas phase it consists of PCl_5 molecules.
	$PCl_3(l) + Cl_2(g) \rightarrow PCl_5(s)$. This reaction is an equilibrium in a closed system.
S	Reacts on heating to give red, covalent liquid.
	$S + Cl_2 \rightarrow SCl_2$

Table 5.5 *Reactions of the elements of Period 3 with water*

Na	Violent reaction at room temperature; metal melts and rushes about the water surface; hydrogen evolved, product solution alkaline. $2Na(s) + 2H_2O(l) \rightarrow 2NaOH(aq) + H_2(g)$
Mg	Extremely slow reaction with cold water. Steam passed over heated metal gives very exothermic reaction (metal glows red) to give the oxide. $Mg(s) + H_2O(g) \rightarrow MgO(s) + H_2(g)$
Al	No reaction with cold water. Steam passed over finely divided heated metal gives the oxide. $2Al(s) + 3H_2O(l) \rightarrow Al_2O_3(s) + 3H_2(g)$
Si P S	} Do not react with water
Cl	Forms acidic solution containing hydrated chlorine molecules as well as chloride and chlorate(I) ions from disproportionation. $Cl_2(g) + H_2O(l) \rightarrow HOCl(aq) + HCl(aq)$

The oxides of Period 3.

The formulae and bonding of the principal oxides, together with their acid/base properties, are given in Figure 5.3.

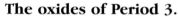

Na	Mg	Al	Si	P	S	Cl
Na_2O	MgO	Al_2O_3	SiO_2	P_4O_6	SO_2	Cl_2O
				P_4O_{10}	SO_3	Cl_2Ol_7
ionic			giant covalent	molecular covalent		
basic		amphoteric		acidic		

Figure 5.3 The oxides of Period 3

The s-block metals have basic oxides, which react with acids to give salts. Aluminium oxide, although ionic, is amphoteric, and will react with both acid and base:

$$Al_2O_3(s) + 6HCl\ (aq) \rightarrow 2AlCl_3(aq) + 3H_2O(l)$$

$$Al_2O_3\ (s) + 3H_2O(l) + 6NaOH(aq) \rightarrow 2Na_3Al(OH)_6(aq)$$

In practice these reactions are difficult to show unless the oxide is freshly prepared. Ageing for a few hours changes the oxide structure to one which is resistant to attack except by concentrated alkali. The amphoteric nature of aluminium oxide classifies aluminium as a semi-metal on chemical grounds, that is, an element whose chemistry shows the characteristics of both metallic and non-metallic elements. If classified on electrical conductivity and other physical properties, aluminium is a metal.

State with reasons what type of bonding you would expect in aluminium fluoride.

Draw a dot-and-cross diagram for aluminium chloride dimer, Al_2Cl_6.

Plot small graphs of
(a) atomic radius,
(b) first ionisation energy, for the elements of period 3, Na to Cl. Comment on any relationship between these graphs.

Look up the melting temperatures of silicon, phosphorus, sulphur and chlorine, and find out why they show the pattern that they do.

The non-metal oxides are all acidic. Silicon dioxide will react with molten sodium hydroxide:

$$SiO_2(s) + 2NaOH(l) \rightarrow Na_2SiO_3(l) + H_2O(g)$$

or with calcium oxide in a blast furnace,

$$SiO_2(s) + CaO(s) \rightarrow CaSiO_3(l)$$

It does not react with aqueous alkali except under pressure at high temperature.

Phosphorus(V) oxide, P_4O_{10}, reacts violently with water to give phosphoric(V) acid

$$P_4O_{10}(s) + 6H_2O(l) \rightarrow 4H_3PO_4(aq)$$

and has such an affinity for water that it makes an excellent, though expensive, drying agent, and will dehydrate concentrated sulphuric acid to sulphur trioxide.

Sulphur dioxide gives sulphurous acid (sulphuric(IV) acid) in water

$$SO_2(g) + H_2O(l) \rightarrow H_2SO_3(aq)$$

though the acid only exists in dilute solution. Sulphur trioxide reacts so violently with water to give sulphuric acid (sulphuric(VI) acid) that in the manufacture of this important material the sulphur trioxide is dissolved in concentrated sulphuric acid which is then diluted with water back to its original concentration. Otherwise a mist of sulphuric acid is formed which is very difficult to handle.

The acid/base nature of oxides thus depends on the character of the element with which the oxygen is combined. The more electropositive this element is, the more basic the oxide, since there is no (or little) covalent bonding and the oxide ion will readily accept hydrogen ions to form water. With the covalent oxides, the bonds with the other element are strong though polar, and there is no oxide ion to receive protons. This results in the reaction with the polar water forming products where covalent bonding between the original element and oxygen survives. For sulphur dioxide in water, therefore:

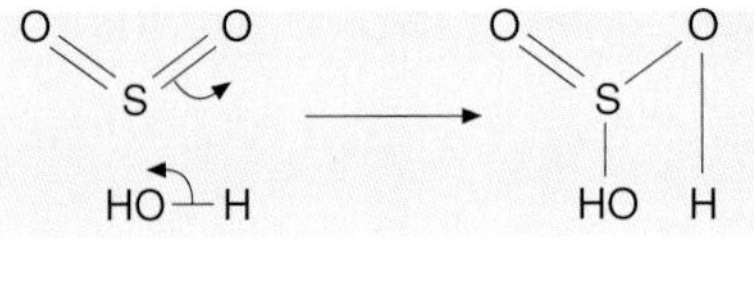

The chlorides of Period 3

The formulae and bonding of the principal chlorides of Period 3 elements are given in Figure 5.4. The formulae of the chlorides show the expected progression based on the group oxidation state of the elements.

Phosphorus and sulphur in higher oxidation states form other chlorides, e.g. PCl_5, SCl_4.

The ionic chlorides dissolve in water to give the hydrated ions and neutral solutions. The covalent chlorides, though, have polar bonds which undergo nucleophilic attack by the lone pair on the water molecule. The reactions are violent apart from that of chlorine, and all apart from chlorine fume in moist air owing to the production of hydrogen chloride droplets.

Look up in a data book the melting and boiling temperatures and density of aluminium and of phosphorus to obtain a comparison of the physical properties of a period 3 metal and non metal.

Na	Mg	Al	Si	P	S	Cl
NaCl	$MgCl_2$	$AlCl_3$	$SiCl_3$	PCl_3	SCl_2	Cl_2
ionic		dimeric covalent	molecular covalent			

Figure 5.4 Chlorides of Period 3 element

The hydrolysis of aluminium chloride proceeds in stages:

$$AlCl_3(s) + H_2O(l) \rightleftharpoons AlCl_2OH(aq) + HCl(aq)$$

$$AlCl_2OH(aq) + H_2O(l) \rightleftharpoons AlCl(OH)_2(aq) + HCl(aq)$$

$$AlCl(OH)_2(aq) + H_2O(l) \rightleftharpoons Al(OH)_3(s) + HCl(aq)$$

In fact aluminium chloride usually produces an acidic solution in water but no precipitate of aluminium hydroxide. The third of these reactions is not therefore very significant unless alkali is added, which will pull the equilibrum over to the product side.

Write equations for the reaction of water and (a) sulphur trioxide to give sulphuric acid, (b) phosphorus (III) oxide to give H_3PO_3, (c) dichlorine oxide to give HOCl.

The same is true for silicon tetrachloride, though in this case the hydrolysis is complete. The product, silica, is initially formed as a hydrate which can be represented as $Si(OH)_4$.

$$SiCl_4(l) + 2H_2O(l) \rightarrow SiO_2(s) + 4HCl(aq)$$

The hydrolysis of the remaining chlorides is represented by:

$$PCl_3(l) + 3H_2O(l) \rightarrow H_3PO_3(aq) + 3HCl(aq)$$

$$2SCl_2(l) + 2H_2O(l) \rightarrow SO_2(aq) + S(s) + 4HCl(aq)$$

$$Cl_2(g) + H_2O(l) \rightarrow HOCl(aq) + HCl(aq)$$

What would you see when SCl_2 is added to water?

Groups 1 and 2: the s-block

The chemistry of the s-block is very simple; trends are clear, and there are very few exceptions to them.

The alkali metals of Group 1 have the electron structure ns^1 outside closed (full) shells; Group 2, the alkaline earth metals, have ns^2. In both cases the only

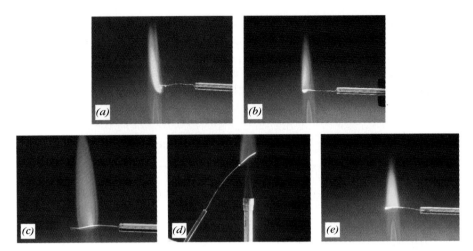

Figure 5.5 The flame colours of: (a) sodium; (b) potassium; (c) calcium; (d) strontium; (e) barium

oxidation state shown is the group state, +1 or +2, and because of effective shielding by the inner electron shells the ionisation energies are low and decrease with increasing size of the atoms. Their compounds are therefore ionic, the relatively low ionisation energies being compensated by high lattice enthalpies of the resulting compounds. The exception to this is beryllium, where the small Be^{2+} ion would have high charge density and be very polarising, so its compounds have a largely covalent character.

Flame colours

Most people are familiar with sodium street lamps and their yellow light. All of the Group 1 elements and three of the Group 2 elements give colours if their atoms are excited by heat or an electric discharge. This effect is used in both qualitative and quantitative analysis, and in the manufacture of fireworks. In qualitative analysis a wire, preferably of platinum, is moistened with concentrated hydrochloric acid, dipped in the salt to be tested, and the sample held to the edge of a roaring bunsen flame (Figure 5.5). The colours obtained are:

Group 1	lithium	carmine red
	sodium	yellow
	potassium	lilac
Group 2	calcium	brick red
	strontium	crimson red
	barium	apple green

The reds are difficult to describe and, in the case of lithium and strontium, difficult to tell apart. In addition most potassium salts have enough sodium contamination to show some yellow; a little sodium gives a lot of colour! Blue glass is sometimes used to filter out the sodium light, the potassium flame then appearing red.

The process is used to measure the amount of sodium or potassium, especially in biological fluids, by the flame photometer. This sprays a solution into the flame, the colour then being filtered by a suitable colour filter and the intensity of the flame colour being measured electronically.

The elements of group 2

The metals of Group 2 are electropositive with low ionisation energy, and react vigorously with oxygen, chlorine and water. The rate increases down the group as the atoms get larger and the ionisation energy therefore gets less. The products are typically ionic, and are colourless. The reactions of calcium are typical:

$$2Ca(s) + O_2(g) \rightarrow 2CaO(s) \text{ on heating}$$

$$Ca(s) + Cl_2(g) \rightarrow CaCl_2(s) \text{ on heating}$$

$$Ca(s) + 2H_2O(l) \rightarrow Ca(OH)_2(aq) + H_2(g) \text{ at room temperature}$$

The oxides of group 2

The oxides of Group 2 are all colourless ionic solids, and apart from the amphoteric beryllium oxide are basic. All but beryllium oxide (which has a high lattice enthalpy) dissolve in water to give solutions of the hydroxides. Water reacts with the small oxide ion which has a high charge density. Calcium oxide is typical:

$$CaO(s) + H_2O(l) \rightarrow Ca(OH)_2(aq)$$

Ionically this is

$$O^{2-} + H_2O \rightarrow 2OH^-$$

This particular reaction is very exothermic, being the process of 'slaking lime'. The oxides all react with aqueous acids to form salts

$$CaO(s) + 2HCl(aq) \rightarrow CaCl_2(aq) + H_2O(l)$$

However, with the exception of magnesium oxide, the reaction with sulphuric acid rapidly stops since the sulphate formed on the oxide surface is sparingly soluble and prevents further attack. The acidic properties of beryllium oxide are not very strong, but it will react with strong alkali to give soluble beryllates:

$$BeO(s) + 2NaOH(aq) + H_2O(l) \rightarrow Na_2Be(OH)_4(aq)$$

Beryllium oxide has been used as a heat-transfer medium in electronics, but, like all other beryllium compounds, it is extremely toxic.

The larger elements in Groups 1 and 2 form oxygen-containing compounds which are not strictly oxides since they do not contain the oxide ion. Sodium and barium form peroxides, Na_2O_2 and BaO_2, which contain O_2^{2-} ions. Here oxygen has an oxidation state of (-1). Potassium and the larger atoms in Group 1 form superoxides such as KO_2; the anion is O_2^-, oxygen having the oxidation state $(-\frac{1}{2})$. In all cases these metals form such compounds with oxygen because of a better size match, and hence a higher lattice enthalpy, with the peroxide and superoxide ions. They are much larger than oxide ions.

Plot on a small graph the first and second ionisation energies of
(a) group 1 and
(b) group 2 elements.

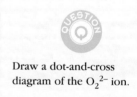

Draw a dot-and-cross diagram of the O_2^{2-} ion.

The chlorides of Groups 1 and 2

The chlorides of Group 1 metals are ionic, colourless solids, soluble in water without hydrolysis. Apart from beryllium chloride, the chlorides of elements in Group 2 are also colourless ionic solids, soluble in water. Beryllium chloride, however, hydrolyses to give beryllium oxide:

$$BeCl_2(s) + H_2O(l) \rightarrow BeO(s) + 2HCl(aq)$$

This is a result of the small size of the beryllium ion which leads to high polarisation of the chloride ion. Beryllium chloride is therefore covalent and thus susceptible to attack by water in the same way as other covalent halides.

Solubility trends in the sulphates and hydroxides of Group 2

We have seen in Chapter 3 how the size of the lattice enthalpies and hydration enthalpies can, for some compounds, give an indication of solubility in water. We shall look at three series of compounds: the Group 2 sulphates where the hydration enthalpy of the cation has most effect, and the Group 1 and 2 hydroxides, where the lattice enthalpy is more important.

Lattice enthalpy is partly a function of the sum of the radii of the anion and the cation, and the size of the sulphate ion is such that this sum doesn't change very much as the cation sizes change. Therefore the contribution from ΔH_{lat} is similar for all of the Group 2 sulphates. However ΔH_{hyd} of the cations falls significantly as they get larger. Thus the solubility of the sulphate also falls as the lattice enthalpy is not exceeded so much by the hydration enthalpies (Table 5.6).

Table 5.6 *Solubilities of Group 2 sulphates*

	Solubility, mol per 100g water	$\Delta H_{hyd}(M^{2+})/$ kJ mol^{-1}	Cation radius/pm
MgSO$_4$	1.83×10^{-1}	-1920	65
CaSO$_4$	4.66×10^{-3}	-1650	99
SrSO$_4$	7.11×10^{-5}	-1480	113
BaSO$_4$	9.43×10^{-7}	-1360	135

This insolubility, particularly for barium sulphate, is made use of in the qualitative test for sulphates. The test solution is made acidic with hydrochloric acid to remove any carbonate or sulphite ions which might be present and which would interfere (white $BaCO_3$ or $BaSO_3$ would precipitate), and then barium chloride solution is added. A white precipitate of barium sulphate is given if sulphate is present:

$$Ba^{2+}(aq) + SO_4^{2-}(aq) \rightarrow BaSO_4(s)$$

This test is positive for hydrogen sulphate ions, HSO_4^-, also. In this case, the original solution will have been very acidic.

Barium sulphate is opaque to X-rays, and is used to show the outline of the gut in radiography. Simple X-rays cannot distinguish the various tissues in the abdomen (and though computer aided X-ray machines can, they are neither cheap nor simple) so barium sulphate is given either as a drink or as an enema. It lines the gut and shows it clearly on the X-ray (Figure 5.6).

In the case of the hydroxides, ΔH_{lat} is the more important factor. This is because the hydroxide ion is quite small, so that the sum of the radii of cation and anion is significantly influenced by the cation size. This is seen clearly in the smaller differences in solubility for hydroxides of the largest cations in Group 2 (Table 5.7). The lattice enthalpies of the hydroxides decrease as the cation gets larger since there is a poorer size match between the cation and anion. ΔH_{lat} decreases more rapidly than the enthalpies of solvation.

The solubilities of Group 1 hydroxides (Table 5.9) are much higher than those of Group 2. The lattice enthalpies are much lower, because the cations are singly charged and thus attract less than is the case with the 2+ ions in Group 2. They are also larger. Although the hydration enthalpies are lower too, they still are larger than the lattice enthalpy. The trend of increasing solubility with increasing cation size matches that of Group 2 for the same reason. The irregularity between potassium and rubidium simply highlights the difficulties of qualitative discussion in circumstances where there are several factors, numerically quite large, where the property depends partly on the differences between them, and a contributing factor (entropy) has been ignored.

THE PERIODIC TABLE

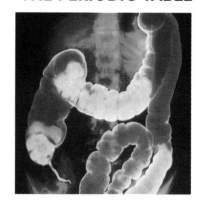

Figure 5.6 Barium sulphate is opaque to X-rays and is used to outline the gut in radiography

Table 5.9 *The solubilities of Group 1 and 2 hydroxides in mol per 100g of water*

Group 1		Group 2	
LiOH	0.516		
NaOH	1.05	$Mg(OH)_2$	2×10^{-5}
KOH	1.71	$Ca(OH)_2$	1.53×10^{-3}
RbOH	1.69	$Sr(OH)_2$	3.37×10^{-3}
CsOH	2.02	$Ba(OH)_2$	1.5×10^{-2}

Trends in thermal stabilities of carbonates and nitrates of Groups 1 and 2

Carbonates decompose on heating, and clear trends are evident. The decomposition of calcium carbonate is typical:

$$CaCO_3(s) \rightarrow CaO(s) + CO_2(g)$$

This reaction is important in cement manufacture and in the extraction of iron.

Since entropy contributions are more or less the same in each case, comparisons of enthalpy effects are quite accurate in these reactions.

The thermal stability of a carbonate will depend on the stability of the carbonate lattice compared with the oxide lattice at the same temperature. As the cation size changes, the lattice enthalpies of the carbonates and those of the oxides change by different factors. The lattice enthalpies of the carbonates change little, since the carbonate ion dominates in size. However the oxide lattice enthalpy falls faster as the cation size increases and there is a poorer size match between big cations and the small oxide ion. The thermal stabilities decrease in the order

$$BaCO_3 \gg SrCO_3 > CaCO_3 > MgCO_3 \gg BeCO_3$$

for Group 2. Barium carbonate does not decompose at bunsen temperatures; all other Group 2 carbonates decompose similarly to $CaCO_3$, as in the equation given above.

Group 1 cations are larger than those of Group 2, and because of the smaller cation charge the lattice enthalpies of the carbonates are smaller too. The result of this is that the differences in lattice enthalpy between the carbonate and the oxide are not sufficient to allow decomposition of the carbonates at normal bunsen temperatures. The exception is lithium carbonate, which has the smallest cation; its carbonate does decompose on heating.

An alternative view of the reasons for thermal decomposition is based on the polarising power of the cation. The larger the metal ion, the lower its polarising power because its charge density is less. Salts of large polarisable anions, e.g. nitrate, carbonate, will be most stable with large, relatively non-polarising cations. Small, polarising cations will favour small anions, since the lattice enthalpy will then be larger.

The nitrates illustrate these points further. Group 2 nitrates all decompose to the metal oxide, brown nitrogen dioxide, and oxygen. Calcium nitrate is typical:

$$2Ca(NO_3)_2(s) \rightarrow 2CaO(s) + 4NO_2(g) + O_2(g)$$

The relatively small cations form stronger lattices with oxide than with the larger nitrate. The decomposition becomes more difficult as the cation size increases, barium nitrate requiring red heat.

In the case of Group 1, the larger cations result in reactions where the product is the nitrite. This is a smaller anion than a nitrate, and so gives a higher lattice enthalpy than nitrates do. But it is not too small, which would be the case with the oxide.

$$2NaNO_3(s) \rightarrow 2NaNO_2(s) + O_2(g)$$

No brown gas is evolved. The nitrates are all white and the nitrites are pale yellow.

This might seem a lot of chemistry; however, comparisons in chemistry, and their explanation, require much time and effort.

Group 4

This interesting group is in the middle of the main group elements (s- and p-blocks) and shows a trend from non-metallic behaviour in carbon to metallic behaviour in lead. Don't be misled by graphite: it's unique and its conductivity

Write the equation for the thermal decomposition of lithium carbonate, Li_2CO_3.

Lithium and magnesium ions have similar charge densities, and show a 'diagonal relationship', that is their chemistries are in some ways similar. Thus $LiNO_3$ decomposes in a similar way on heating to that of group 2 nitrates. Write an equation for its decomposition.

isn't like that of metals, nor is it nearly as good (see Chapter 3). There is also a change from the dominance of oxidation state +4 in carbon to +2 in lead.

The Elements
The character of the elements is as follows

carbon	non-metal
silicon	non-metallic chemically, semi-metal physically
germanium	semi-metal
tin	weakly electropositive metal
lead	weakly electropositive metal

The elements of Group 4, being much less electropositive than those of Groups 1 and 2, either do not react or do so slowly with chlorine, oxygen or water.

With oxygen, heating is required and all but lead give the dioxide. Silicon is typical:

$$Si(s) + O_2(g) \rightarrow SiO_2(s).$$

Lead(II) oxide, PbO, is formed slowly on heating lead in air.

Chlorine does not react directly with carbon; the other elements give the tetrachloride on heating, again except for lead which gives lead(II) chloride, $PbCl_2$. These anomalies of lead arise from the greater stability of the +2 state compared with +4, which is dealt with below.

Water reacts at high temperature with carbon in a strongly endothermic reaction to give carbon monoxide:

$$C(s) + H_2O(g) \rightarrow CO(g) + H_2(g)$$

This gas was at one time a very useful industrial fuel called water gas. The other elements do not react significantly with water.

The oxides of Group 4
Group 4 elements have a wider variety of oxides than those of Group 2. Their properties are summarised in Table 5.8.

The acidity of carbon dioxide is shown in its reaction with water to give a solution which, when saturated with the gas, is around pH 5, being carbonic acid:

$$CO_2(g) + H_2O(l) \rightleftharpoons H^+(aq) + HCO_3^-(aq)$$

$$HCO_3^-(aq) \rightleftharpoons H^+(aq) + CO_3^{2-}(aq)$$

Carbonic acid forms two series of salts, the hydrogen carbonates (bicarbonates) such as $NaHCO_3$, and the carbonates, formed by nearly all metals. Aluminium and beryllium are notable exceptions.

Table 5.8 *The oxides of Group 4*

Oxide	Physical properties and bonding	Acid/base character	Other properties
CO	Colourless gas, molecular	Neutral	Very toxic, odourless
(SiO)	Probably a mixture of Si and SiO_2		
GeO	White solid, ionic	Amphoteric	Oxidises in air
SnO	White solid, ionic	Amphoteric	Oxidises in air
PbO	Yellow solid, ionic	Amphoteric	
CO_2	Colourless gas, molecular	Acidic	
SiO_2	Colourless solid, giant molecular	Acidic	
GeO_2	Grey-white solid, ionic with covalent character	Amphoteric	
SnO_2	White solid, ionic with covalent character.	Amphoteric	
PbO_2	Chocolate brown solid, ionic with covalent character	Amphoteric	Strongly oxidising

Carbon monoxide is, in principle, the anhydride of methanoic acid, and might be expected to react with water according to the equation:

$$CO + H_2O \rightarrow HCOOH$$

Carbon monoxide can be made by the dehydration of methanoic acid with concentrated sulphuric acid. However, carbon monoxide is inert to water, and the above reaction does not occur. It will react with aqueous sodium hydroxide under pressure at high temperature to give sodium methanoate

$$CO(g) + NaOH(aq) \rightarrow HCOONa(aq)$$

but the acidic properties of carbon monoxide are so weak that it is regarded as a neutral oxide.

Silicon(IV) oxide, silica, is acidic, but it is so insoluble in water that it does not noticeably react with aqueous alkali. It does not interfere with the purification of bauxite for aluminium production (Topic 21, Module 3) since the 10% aqueous solution of sodium hydroxide used in current practice does not dissolve the silica impurity in the bauxite. Silica will react with molten sodium hydroxide to give sodium silicate, Na_2SiO_3, which is an ingredient of detergents for dishwashers. In the blast furnace the reaction with calcium oxide is important in removing SiO_2 impurity from the iron ore and enabling a continuous process to occur (see the section on the Oxides of Period 3, and Topic 21 of Module 3).

The amphoteric nature of lead (II) oxide is shown by the following reactions.

As a base, the reaction

$$PbO(s) + 2HCl(aq) \rightarrow PbCl_2(s) + H_2O(l)$$

occurs. In practice if concentrated hydrochloric acid is used solutions of complexes such as $PbCl_3^-$ and $PbCl_4^{2-}$ are obtained. These precipitate white lead(II) chloride, $PbCl_2$, on dilution. The reaction of lead(II) oxide with sulphuric acid stops almost immediately since lead sulphate, $PbSO_4$, is insoluble. With alkali lead(II) oxide reacts as an acid and the soluble plumbate(II) is formed:

$$PbO(s) + 2NaOH(aq) + H_2O(l) \rightarrow Na_2Pb(OH)_4(aq)$$

The chlorides of Group 4

The principal features of Group 4 chlorides are summarised in Table 5.9 together with the bond type and the reaction with water. Germanium chlorides are unimportant.

Table 5.9 *The chlorides of Group 4*

Carbon			CCl_4	Covalent liquid, unreactive below 1000°C
Silicon			$SiCl_4$	Covalent liquid, hydrolyses
Germanium	$GeCl_2$	Ionic, hydrolyses	$GeCl_4$	Covalent liquid, hydrolyses
Tin	$SnCl_2$	Ionic, hydrolyses	$SnCl_4$	Covalent liquid, hydrolyses
Lead	$PbCl_2$	Ionic, insoluble	$PbCl_4$	Covalent liquid, unstable above 0°C, hydrolyses

The smaller atoms in Group 4 give halides in oxidation state +2 which hydrolyse in water, though not completely. They form basic chlorides:

$$SnCl_2(s) + H_2O(l) \rightleftharpoons SnClOH(s) + HCl(aq)$$

The cloudy liquid which results can be cleared by the addition of concentrated hydrochloric acid, which shifts this equilibrium to the left-hand side. Solutions of tin(II) chloride must, therefore, be acidic if hydrolysis is to be avoided. The tetrahalides show marked differences in properties. Tetrachloromethane, CCl_4, is not attacked by water at room temperature, and even at 1000°C it hydrolyses only partially:

$$CCl_4(g) + H_2O(g) \rightarrow COCl_2(g) + 2HCl(g)$$

The product, carbonyl chloride, is extremely toxic and has been used in warfare as a poison gas. The resistance of tetrachloromethane to hydrolytic attack is a consequence firstly of the strength of the carbon–chlorine bond, which has to be broken before further reaction can occur, and secondly of the lack of any vacant orbitals through which the attacking water nucleophile can coordinate. This is a very significant feature of carbon chemistry generally; most carbon compounds are thermodynamically unstable with respect to oxidation or hydrolysis, yet life goes on in the presence of a good deal of oxygen and water. The lack of such vacant orbitals for attack renders most carbon compounds kinetically stable, that is the reactions are far too slow to be observed. Just as well for all of us!

THE PERIODIC TABLE

Draw the full structural formula for carbonyl chloride, $COCl_2$. State its shape, with reasons.

The position changes abruptly with the heavier elements of Group 4, from silicon on. Now the possibility of using empty d-orbitals arises, and the rapid attack of water on silicon tetrachloride is due to one of the lone electron pairs of the attacking water molecule being coordinated to the silicon atom before the Si–Cl bond is broken. The energy barrier to reaction is therefore much lower, and so the reaction is dramatically faster. The reaction of silicon tetrachloride with water is typical of the tetrahalides:

$$SiCl_4(l) + 2H_2O(l) \rightarrow SiO_2(s) + 4HCl(aq)$$

Oxidation states in Group 4

The smaller elements of Group 4 show a wide range of oxidation states, carbon having +4 in CO_2, +2 in CO, and –4 in CH_4. Tin and lead show +4 and +2, and the trend is for +2 to be more stable as the group is descended. In practice the difference is seen between tin and lead; tin(IV) oxide is not an oxidising agent, and reacts with cold hydrochloric acid to give tin(IV) chloride in an acid–base reaction:

$$SnO_2(s) + 4HCl(aq) \rightarrow SnCl_4(l) + 2H_2O(l)$$

Tin(II) is however reducing, and is used for example to reduce nitrobenzene to phenylamine, an important material in dyestuffs manufacture. The reaction is effected by heating in concentrated hydrochloric acid:

$$C_6H_5NO_2 + 3Sn^{2+} + 6H^+ \rightarrow C_6H_5NH_2 + 2H_2O + 3Sn^{4+}$$

Phenylamine is produced as the water-soluble hydrochloride salt $C_6H_5NH_3^+Cl^-$, and is liberated by the addition of aqueous sodium hydroxide.

Lead(IV) oxide is an oxidising agent because lead(II) is the more stable state, so, with concentrated hydrochloric acid at room temperature, chlorine is formed by oxidation of chloride ions:

$$PbO_2(s) + 4HCl(aq) \rightarrow PbCl_2(s) + Cl_2(g) + 2H_2O(l).$$

Lead(II) is not reducing.

The explanation of these effects is given in Topic 21 of Module 3.

Questions

1 *(a)* Define **oxidation** in terms of electron transfer   **(1)**

(b) State **three** properties which distinguish transition metals from main group metals.   **(3)**

(c) Give the electronic configurations for Fe and Fe^{3+} in the table below.

		3d				4s	

Fe: (Ar)

Fe^{3+}:   (Ar)

Suggest why Fe^{3+} is more stable ion than Fe^{2+} under normal conditions.   **(3)**

(d) (i) Name the types of reacton involved in the following changes:

$$[Cu(H_2O)6]^{2+} \quad \xrightarrow{\text{aqueous NH}_3} \quad \text{blue precipitate} \quad \xrightarrow{\text{aqueous NH}_3} \quad \text{deep blue solution}$$
$$\textbf{A} \qquad\qquad\qquad\qquad \textbf{B} \qquad\qquad\qquad\qquad \textbf{C}$$

   A to **B**:

   B to **C**:

   (ii) Give the formula of compound B.

   (iii) Draw the structure of the ion responsible for the colour in solution C and show its shape.   **(5)**

(e) Addition of aqueous copper(II) ions to aqueous iodide ions gives a precipitate of copper(I) iodide and liberates iodine; the iodine can be titrated with aqueous sodium thiosulphate, so these reactions form the basis for a volumetric analysis of copper, for example in metal alloys.

   (i) Write an ionic equation for the reaction of copper(II) ions with iodide ions.

   (ii) Given theat the reaction of iodine with sodium thiosulphate is

$$I_2(aq) + 2S_2O^2_3{}^- (aq) \; 2I^-(aq) + S_4O^2_6{}^-(aq)$$

   find the volume of sodium thiosulphate solution of concentration 1.00 mol dm^{-3} needed to react with the iodine liberated by copper ions from a brass screw of mass 2.00 g, containing 60% of copper by mass.   **(4)**

TOTAL 16 marks

(ULEAC GCE Chemistry (9081/8081), June 1995)

QUESTIONS

2 *(a)* Enter the formulae of the oxides for the elements shown in the empty boxes in the top two rows of the table below. Indicate in the bottom row of boxes the acid-base nature of these oxides.

Na	Mg	Al	Si	P	S	Cl

(4)

(b) Group 4 elements show a trend from non-metallic to metallic behaviour with increasing atomic number. How is this shown by the acid-base properties of carbon dioxide, CO_2, silicon dioxide, SiO_2, and lead(II) oxide, PbO? Write equations to illustrate this behaviour. **(5)**

(c) PbO and PbO_2 differ strikingly in their properties. Illustrate this by giving the reactions between these two oxides and concentrated HCl, stating the nature of each reaction.

For PbO:

For PbO_2: **(4)**

(d) The +2 oxidation state of tin is reducing. Give a reaction to illustrate this property. **(2)**

TOTAL 15 marks

(ULEAC GCE Chemistry (9081/8081), June 1995)

3 *(a)* The main ore of lead is galena, lead(II) sulphide.

To produce lead, this ore is heated in air, when some of the lead(II) sulphide is converted to lead(II) oxide and sulphur dioxide.

The air supply is then cut off and on further heating the lead(II) oxide is converted, by reaction with the remaining lead(II) sulphide, to lead and sulphur dioxide.

Write an equation for (i) the conversion of galena to lead(II) oxide and (II) the reaction of lead(II) oxide with lead(II) sulphide. **(2)**

(b) Calculate the total volume (m^3) of sulphur dioxide which would be produced from 5.0×10^3 kg of galena in the reactions described in *(a)*. (Assume that one mole of any gas occcupies 2.4×10^{-2} ;m^3 at room temperature and pressure.) **(3)**

(c) (i) Another compound of lead Z, which is found naturally contains 77.5% of lead and 4.5% of carbon by mass, the remainder being assumed to be oxygen. Calculate the empirical formula of the compound.

(ii) 0.0500 mol of this compound Z gives, on heating, 11.2 g of lead(II) oxide and a gas is evolved. What is the molecular formula of compound Z? **(4)**

(d) (i) The compound Z reacts with nitric acid to form a solution containing only lead(II) nitrate. When aqueous sodium chloride is added to the solution, a white precipitate forms. Write an ionic equation for this precipitation reaction.

    (ii)   What is the concentration (mol dm^{-3}) of a solution containing
           5.00 g of lead(II) nitrate in 200 cm^3 of solution?

    (iii)   State the shape of the nitrate ion, briefly giving your reasons. **(6)**

TOTAL 15 marks

(ULEAC GCE Chemistry (9081/8081), January 1996)

4 *(a)* Draw a diagram to show the arrangement of ions in the sodium
      chloride crystal. **(2)**

(b) Identify the products of the action of heat on
    (i)   lithium carbonate:
    (ii)   magnesium nitrate:
    (iii)   strontium nitrae: **(3)**

(c) A solution contains 50.5 g dm^{-3} of the chloride of an alkaline earth
      metal. To 25.0 cm^3 of this solution was added an excess of acqueous
      silver nitrate; 3.77 g of silver chloride, AgC1, was precipitated. Calculate
      the value of the relative atomic mass of the metal and suggest its
      identity. **(5)**

(d) Write ionic equations for the following reactions:
    (i)   the precipitation of silver chloride from the solution containing
         the metal chloride in *(c)*;
    (ii)   the formation of a white precipitate when acqueous sodium
         hydroxide is added to the solution containing the metal chloride
         in *(c)*. **(2)**

(e) Give ONE property of each substance which makes it suitable for the
      particular application.
    (i)   Magnesium oxide in furnace linings:
    (ii)   The addition of calcium hydroxide to soil:
    (iii)   The potential use of sodium metal in electricity cables: **(3)**

TOTAL 15 marks

(ULEAC GCE Chemistry (9081/8081), January 1996)

5 *(a)* Give the electron structure of the vanadium atom and the V^{2+} ion:

		3d					4s
V:	(Ar)						
V^{2+}:	(Ar)						

(2)

(b) (i) Suggest why the hydrated ion $[V(H_2O)_6]^{2+}$ is coloured.
    (ii) Name the types of bonding within ions of this type. **(3)**

(c) Ammonium vanadate, NH_4VO_3, dissolves in acqueous sodium
      hydroxide with the evolution of a colourless gas. The solution
      becomes yellow after acidification. The gas has a pungent odour and
      produces a pale blue precipitate with copper(II) sulphate solution. The
      precipitate dissolves as more gas is passed in, to give a deep blue
      solution.
    (i)   Write an ionic equation for the reaction of the cation in NH_4VO_3
         with alkali.
    (ii)   Name the pale blue precipitate.

(iii) Give the formula of the ion responsible for the colour of the deep blue solution.

(iv) Ammonium vanadate, on treatment with sulphuric acid, gives a yellow colour due to the $[VO_2]^+$ ion. Addition of zinc to the solution causes the solution colour to change to blue, then green, then violet. Give the oxidation number of vanadium in the vanadium-containing ions in each coloured solution.

Blue solution:

Green solution:

Violet solution: **(5)**

(d) The industrial production of sulphur trioxide from sulphur dioxide and oxygen is catalysed by vanadium(V) oxide. It has been proposed that the first stage of the reaction is

$$SO_2 + V_2O_5 \rightarrow SO_3 + 2VO_2$$

Write an equation for the second stage, thus showing the behaviour of vanadium(V) oxide as a catalyst. **(1)**

(e) Give the systematic name for each of these ions:

(i) $[VO_2]+$:

(ii) $[Cr(NH_3)_4Cl_2]^+$: **(2)**

(f) Draw and describe the shape of the ion in (e)(ii). **(2)**

TOTAL 15 marks

ULEAC GCE Chemistry (9081/8081), January 1996

6 Hydrogen peroxide, which is used extensively for bleaching, is manufactured by a process involving 2-ethylanthraquinone. This latter compound may be represented by the formula O=X=O, where X is a complex organic group.

(a) In the first stage of the process hydrogen gas is reacted with a solution of the 2-ethylanthraquinone in an organic solvent, in the presence of a small quantity of nickel. 2-ethylanthraquinol is formed:

$$O=X=O +H_2 \rightarrow HO–X–OH$$

What type of reaction is this and what is the purpose of the nickel?

Type of reaction:

Purpose of nickel: **(2)**

(b) The 2-ethylanthraquinol is then reacted with oxygen to produce hydrogen peroxide and the 2-theylanthraaquinone is reformed:

$$HO–X–OH + O_2 \rightarrow O=X=O + H_2O_2$$

Calculate the volume of oxygen (dm^3 at room temperature and pressure) which would be needed to produce 1.00 tonne of hydrogen peroxide.

(The volume occupied by 1 mole of oxygen molecules at room temperature and pressure is 24 dm^3; 1 tonne = 10^6 g.) **(3)**

(c) By adding water the hydrogen peroxide is extracted as an aqueous solution containing 20% hydrogen peroxide by mass. Calculate the concentration in mol dm^{-3} of this solution (1.00 cm^3 of the solution has a mass of 1.07 g). **(3)**

(d) A student diluted 25.0 cm^3 of a solution of hydrogen peroxide to 250 cm^3. When 20.0 cm^3 of the diluted solution was acidified, it required 19.2 cm^3 of 0.0210 mol dm^{-3} potassium manganate(VII) for oxidation. Calculate the concentration (mol dm$^{-3)}$ of the original hydrogen peroxide solution.
The relevant equation is:

$$MnO^-_4 + 6H^+ + 5H_2O_2 \rightarrow 2Mn^{2+} + 8H_2O + 5O_2 \qquad \textbf{(4)}$$

(e) The Mn^{3+} ion, stable in a strongly acidic solution, disproportionates when the solution is diluted. Construct balanced half-equations for the following:
   (i)   the conversion of Mn^{3+} ions to Mn^{2+} ions;
   (ii) the conversion of Mn^{3+} ions to managanese(IV) oxide. **(2)**

(f) Write down the overall equation for the disproportionation in *(e)*. **(1)**

TOTAL 15 marks

(ULEAC GCE Chemistry (9081/8081), January 1995)

7 *(a)* Identify the solid remaining when each of the following is heated.
Lithium nitrate:
Potassium nitrate:
Calcium nitrate: **(3)**

(b) (i) When calcium oxide and coke are heated in an electric furnace, the products are carbon monoxide and calcium dicarbide (CaC$_2$). Write the equation for this reaction.

   (ii) Addition of water to calcium dicarbide leads to the formation of calcium hydroxide and ethyne (ethyne has the formula C$_2$H$_2$ and is the starting point for the manufacture of a variety of substances, including rayon and PVC). Write the equation for the production of ethyne.

   (iii) Until recently most ethyne was made in industry by the method in (ii). Today, ethyne is produced in industry by heating methane (CH$_4$) alone at a high temperature for 0.01 second. Write an equation for this reaction.

   (iv) Draw a diagram showing the electron arrangement in the dicarbide ion C$_2^{2-}$. **(5)**

(c) Describe how, by a chemical test, you could distinguish between the two compounds in each of the following pairs. Give the expected result for each substance. Two different tests should be described.
   (i) Lithium carbonate and magnestium carbonate.
   (ii) Calcium carbonate and barium carbonate. **(5)**

TOTAL 13 marks

(ULEAC GCE Chemistry (9081/8081), January 1995)

QUESTIONS

8 *(a)* (i) Draw a clear diagram to show the shape of the ammonia molecule.
Indicate on the diagram the approximate bond angles.

    (ii) Give an example of this shape. **(4)**

(b) The following ions may be formed as intermediates in chemical reactions. Their shapes can be predicted in the usual way. Draw a clear diagram of each, indicating values for the bond angles.

    (i) CH_3^- (ii) CH_3^+ **(4)**

(c) Sodium chloride is ionic, whereas aluminium chloride is predominantly covalent, yet sodium and aluminium are both metals. Give an explanation for this. **(4)**

(d) Briefly explain why, although a large amount of energy is required to separate the ions in solid sodium chloride, sodium chloride dissolves in water with little change in temperature. **(2)**

(e) Write equations to show why the action of a large volume of water on anhydrous aluminium chloride results in an acidic solution. **(2)**

TOTAL 16 marks

(ULEAC GCE Chemistry (9081/8081), January 1995)

Index

Page references in *italics* refer to a table or an illustration.

α-particles 3, 9, 11
acids, titrations with 27–32
alkali earth metals *see* Group 2
alkali metals *see* Group 1
alkalis 58–60, *60*
   see also bases
alpha decay 9
alpha particles 3, 9, 11
aluminium 3, 69, 71
   see also Period 3
ammonia
   hydrogen bonding in 40
   reactions with transition metals
      59–60, *60*
anions 34–6
aqua complexes 57, 58–60, 60
atomic number 5
atomic orbitals 20–1, *20*, 37–8
atomic structure 2–21
aufbau principle 17–20, *18*
auto-analyser *22*
Avogadro, Amadeo 25
Avogadro constant 25–6

β-particles 9, 11
back-titrations 29–30, 31–2
Balmer, J.J. 3
Balmer series 4, *4*
barium 74–5, 75
bases
   titrations with 27–32
   see also alkalis
Becquerel, A.H. 3
beryllium 72, 73, 74
   see also Group 2
beta particles 9, 11
Bohr, Niels 3–5, *4*, 20
boiling *44*
   effect of intermolecular forces 40,
      40, 41, 43, *43*
bond pairs 37, 46–8
bonds and bonding
   change of state 44–6
   covalent bonds 36–9
   electronegativity 38, *38*, 51–2
   hydrogen bonding 39–40, *39*, 43
   intermolecular bonds 39–43

ionic bonds 34–6, 41–2
   electron density map *35*
   solubility of ionic compounds
      44–6
   metallic 48–9
   orbitals in 37–8, *37*
   polarity 38–9, *39*
   shapes of molecules and ions *37*,
      41, 46–8, *47*
branching chain reactions 12–13

calcium 2, 73, 75
   see also Group 2
calculations 22–33
carbon 6, 12, 15
   diamond 41, *41*
   graphite 41, *41*, 49
   see also Group 4
carbon dioxide 77
carbon monoxide 78
carbonates 75–6
catalysis 63–4, *64*
cathode rays 2, *2*
cations 34–6
   of transition metals 57–64, *57*
Chadwick, James 5, *5*, 12
chain reactions 12–13
chlorides
   of Group 4 79–80, *79*
   of Groups 1 and 2 *36*, 45, 74
   of Period 3 *68*, 70–1, *71*
chlorine 8
   reactions with 68, 77
   see also Group 7; Period 3
cis isomers 57
cloud chambers *10*
colours
   flame colours 72, *72*
   of ions 57–8
complex ions 35, 57–60, *57*
compounds 8, 22–3, *22*
concentration 27–32
conductivity 41–2, 48–9
copper 48, *49*, 56, *56*
   see also transition metals
covalent bonds 36–9
Curie, Pierre and Marie 2, 3

d-block 18–19, *55*
   electronic configurations 55
   see also transition metals
Dalton, John 2, *2*
dative covalent bonds 36–7
decay, radioactive 9–12, *9*, *10*, *11*
   half-life 13–14, *14*
   thorium series 9, *10*, 11–12
Democritus 2
diamond 41, *41*
dichromate(VI) 51, 53–4
dipoles 39–41, *39*, *43*
dispersion forces 41
double bonds 37–8, *37*

electromagnetic radiation 10–11
electron affinity 21, *21*
electronegativity 38, *38*, 51–2
electronic structures 16–20, *19*, 55, *55*
electrons
   in atomic structure 3–5, *4*, 15–21
   beta particles 9, 11
   cathode rays 2, *2*
   in covalent bonds 36
   electron density map *35*
   in graphite 41, 49
   in metals 48
   properties of *5*, 6
   in redox reactions 50
   transitions of 3–5, *4*, 57–8
   see also ionisation energy
elements 5, 50
empirical formulae 22, 23
energy
   electron gain energy 21
   in electron transitions 3–5, *4*, 57–8
   in gamma emission 10–11
   ionisation energy 15–17
      of transition metals 56, *56*
   released by fusion 13
enthalpy
   hydration enthalpies 44–6, *46*
   lattice enthalpies 35–6, *36*, 44–6, *45*
equations 11–12, 23–5
ethanol 8, *8*
evaporation 44
explosions 12–13, *13*
exponential decay 13–14

INDEX

flame colours 72, *72*
fluorine 7, 51
   see also Group 7
forces, intermolecular 39–43
formula mass 6
formulae 22–3
fusion, nuclear 13

γ-emission 10–11
gamma rays 10–11
gases
   in calculations 32–3
   helium (α-particles) 3, 9, 11
   hydrogen *see* hydrogen
   noble 43, *43*
     neon 8, *8*
   oxygen *see* oxygen
   spectra of 3–4, *4*
   vapours 44
germanium *66*
   see also Group 4
graphite 41, *41*, 49
Group 1 (alkali metals) 16–17
   hydration enthalpies *46*
   lattice enthalpies *45*
   trends in 71–2, 74, 75–6, *75*
Group 2 (alkali earth metals) 71–4
   enthalpies *36*, *45*, *46*
   solubility 74–5, *74*, *75*
   thermal stability 75–6
Group 4 76–80, *78*, *79*
   carbon *see* carbon
   germanium *66*
   hydrides 43, *43*
Groups 5 and 6 39–40, *40*
   phosphorus 12, 15, 70
Group 7 (halogens) 17
   chlorine *see* chlorine
   fluorine 51
   hydration enthalpies *46*
   hydrogen bonding in 39–40, *40*
   lattice enthalpies *36*
Group 8 (noble gases) 43, *43*
   neon 8, *8*

half-life 13–14, *14*
half-reactions 52–4, *54*
halides *see* Group 7
halogens *see* Group 7
helium nucleus (α-particles) 3, 9, 11
Hess's law 45

history of atomic structure 2–5
hydration of ions 44–6, *46*
hydrides
   of Group 4 43, *43*
   of Groups 5, 6 and 7 39–40, *40*, 43
hydrogen
   atomic orbitals 20, *20*
   ionisation energy *16*
   oxidation state 51–2
   spectra 3, *4*
hydrogen bonding 39–40, *39*, 43
hydrogen fluoride 39, *39*
hydrogen peroxide 53–4
hydroxides 74–5, *75*

intermolecular bonds 39–43
intramolecular bonds 39
ionic bonds 34–6, 41–2
   solubility of ionic compounds 44–6
ionic equations 24–5
ionisation energy 15–17, *16*
   of transition metals 56–7, *56*
ionising radiations 11
ions 34–5
   aqua complexes 57, 58–60, *60*
   coloured 57–8
   complex ions 35, 57–60, *57*
   in equations 24–5
   paramagnetism in 58
   shapes of 46–8, *47*
   in solutions 44–6
   of transition metals 35, 57–64, *57*
iron 62–3, *63*
   see also transition metals
isomerism 57
isotopes 6, 14–15

JET project 13

Kolbe, Hermann 46

lattice enthalpy 35–6, *36*, 44–6
   effect on solubility 74–5
lead 77, 78–9, *78*
   see also Group 4
ligand exchange 60
ligands 35, 57
liquids 43, 44
   see also boiling; melting; solutions
lone pairs 37, 46–8
Loschmidt's number 25

manganate(VII) 51, 52–3
mass
   in calculations 25–7
   in energy conversion 13
mass difference 13
mass number 6
mass spectrometry 6–8, 7, 9
melting 41, 44
Mendeleyev, D.I. 65, *65*
metals
   bonding in 48–9
   copper 48, *49*, 56, *56*
   lead 77, 78–9, *78*
     see also Group 4
   silver 48, *49*
   transition *see* transition metals
   uranium 3, 11, *11*, 12–13
   zinc 55
molar mass 25–7
molar volume of gases 32–3, *33*
molecular formulae 23
molecules
   bonding 36–9, 41, 42–3
     polarity in 38–41, *39*
   giant molecular substances 41, *41*
   intermolecular forces 39–43
   mass spectroscopy of 8
   shapes of *37*, *41*, 46–8, *47*
moles 25–7

neon 8, *8*
   see also noble gases
neutrons 5–6, *5*, 12
nitrates 76
noble gases 43, *43*
   neon 8, *8*
nuclear energy 9, 12–13
nuclear equations 11–12
nuclear fusion 13
nuclear reactions 12–13
nuclear weapons 12–13
nucleus
   stability and decay 6, 9–11
   structure 2–3, 5–6
nuclides 6, 14–15

orbitals 17–21
   in covalent bonds 37–8
   shapes *20*
organic compounds
   mass spectroscopy of 8, *8*
   proteins 42

oxidation numbers 50–4, 57, 80
oxidation and reduction 50–4
   half-reactions 52–4, *54*
   redox titrations 32
oxidation states 50–4, 57, 80
oxides
   of Group 2 73
   of Group 4 77–9, *78*
   lattice enthalpies for *45*
   of Period 3 69–70, *69*
oxidising agents 53–4
oxygen
   oxidation state of 51, 52
   reactions with *68*, 77

π-bonds 37–8, *37*
p-block 18
paramagnetism 58
particles
   alpha and beta 3, 9, 11
   electrons *see* electrons
   of nucleus 2–3, 5–6, *5*, 12
   and waves 20
Pauling, Linus *37*, 38
penetration (of radiation) 11
Period 3 65, 67–71, *68*, *69*, *71*
Periodic Table 65–80, *66*
   and electronegativity 38, *38*
   and ionisation energy 16–17
   Mendeleyev's table 65
phosphorus 12, 15, 70
   see also Group 5; Period 3
pi bonds 37–8, *37*
polarisation 35–6, *35*, 76
polarity 38–9, *39*
polymers 42–3
proteins 42
protons 2–3, 5–6, *5*

quantitative chemistry 22–33

radiation
   UK exposure to 9, *9*
   see also radioactivity
radii
   and electronegativity 38
   in ionic bonding 35–6
   of transition metals 56, *56*
radioactivity 3, 6, 8–15
   decay 9–12, *9*, *10*, *11*
      thorium series *9*, *10*, 11–12

half-life 13–14, *14*
   radiotherapy 15, *15*
radionuclides 6, 14–15
radiotherapy 15, *15*
range (ionising radiation) 11
reactions
   chain 12–13
   redox *see* oxidation and reduction
redox reactions *see* oxidation and
      reduction
reducing agents 51, 52–3
reduction *see* oxidation and
      reduction
relative atomic mass 6, 8
relative molecular mass 6
Rutherford, Ernest 3

σ-bonds 37–8
s-block 18, 71–6
scandium 55
Schrödinger, E. 20
science, study of 1–2, 22
shapes, molecules and ions *37*, *41*,
      46–8, *47*
shell model 3–4, 15
   subshells and orbitals 17–21, *20*, 37–8
sigma bonds 37–8
silicon 3, 77, 78, 80
   see also Group 4; Period 3
silver 48, *49*
size (atoms and ions) *see* radii
sodium chloride 34, *34*, *35*
sodium hydroxide 59, *60*
solids, change of state of 44
solubility
   hydrogen bonding increases 40
   of ionic compounds 44–6
   trends 74–5, *74*, *75*
solutions
   calculations involving 27–33
   standard solutions 28
   see also liquids
spectator ions 24
spectra
   of gases 3–4, *4*
   mass 7–8, *8*
spectrometry
   of gases 3–4, *4*
   mass 6–8, *7*, *9*
stability, of nuclei 6, 9–11
standard solutions 28

state, change of 44–6
strong nuclear force 9
strontium-90 12
subshells and orbitals 17–21, 37–8
sulphates 74–5, *74*

thermal stability 75–6
Thomson, J.J. 2–3
thorium decay series 9, *10*, 11–12
titrations 27–32
trans isomers 57
transition metals 55
   catalytic activity of 63–4, *64*
   complex ions 35, 57–60, *57*
   copper 48, *49*, 56, *56*
   ionisation energy 56–7, *56*
   iron 62–3, *63*
   reactions with alkalis 58–60, *60*
   vanadium 56, *56*, 61–2, *61*
triple bonds 37–8, *37*

uranium 3, 11, *11*, 12–13

van der Waals' forces 39, 41, 43
vanadium 56, *56*, 61–2, *61*
   see also transition metals
van't Hoff, J.H. 46, *46*
vapours 44
   see also gases
volumes of gases 32–3
volumetric analysis 27–32

water
   hydrogen bonding in 40
   reactions with *69*, 73, 77
   see also solubility
waves, electrons as 20

Ziegler and Natta 42
zinc 55